OCD Workbook for Adults

Overcome Obsessive Compulsive Disorder Using CBT & DBT Skills for Disruptive Thoughts & Behaviors | Mindfulness, Emotion Regulation & Coping Strategies for Men & Women

By Barrett Huang
https://barretthuang.com/

FREE Guide: Mastering DBT Essentials

FREE DOWNLOAD ALERT!

Master Dialectical Behavior Therapy Skills in 5 Simple Steps with my Free DBT Quick Guide. Access the 'Mastering DBT Essentials' quick guide at:

https://barretthuang.com/dbt-quick-guide/

Or scan the code below:

SCAN ME

Contents

Introduction

"It's like you have two brains — a rational brain and an irrational brain. And they're constantly fighting."
— Emilie Ford

A Snapshot of My Life as a Teenager with OCD

The alarm goes off, and I grudgingly reach out to turn it off so it doesn't wake up the whole household. It's only 6 AM, after all, a school day.

Although classes don't start till 9 AM, I MUST get up early to do my self-imposed morning routine. Otherwise, my whole day will be ruined. My morning routine goes like this, more or less.

6:00 AM – Get up and go to the bathroom.
6:15 AM – Get dressed for school.
6:30 AM – Go down and get some breakfast.
6:45 AM – Return to my room and do my "poster ritual."
7:45 AM – Leave for school <u>IF</u> my poster ritual goes well.

What's the poster ritual, and why does it take me nearly two hours?

In the late 1990s, there was a popular British pop girl band called the *Spice Girls,* and at 14, I had a huge crush on Emma Bunton (a.k.a. Baby Spice). The crush turned into an obsession, and by the time I was 15, I had several posters of her in my room and a full-blown poster ritual that I MUST do every morning.

This involved standing before Emma Bunton's poster and "talking" to her. I would pretend I was courting her (never mind that she was much older than me). Various conversations and scenarios between us would ebb and flow in my mind.

This would go on until I felt "just right." It's hard to explain, but I HAD to feel that Emma and I were "okay" and things were right between us. Once I reach this feeling, then and only then can I leave the house for school.

Sometimes, my poster ritual would only take 5-10 minutes. Other times, it would take HOURS. That's why I need to wake up very early.

Obviously, this obsession and compulsion had a huge negative impact on my teen life. I was always late for school because I had to get the "right feeling" before stopping the routine and leaving the house. I often skipped sleep altogether because I didn't want to repeat the whole morning poster ritual the next day. As a result, I was often sleep-deprived and felt like I had no energy throughout the day.

I would skip school if I didn't get the feeling of harmony I was looking for with Emma. This is because I was afraid something bad would happen or I wouldn't get that particular feeling ever again, so I would keep doing it, for hours on end if I had to, to reassure myself that everything in life would be okay.

My morning poster ritual is just one of the manifestations of my Obsessive-Compulsive Disorder (OCD). I had many others.

When I was about 7 or 8, I engaged in chronic nail picking (*onychotillomania*). I would constantly pick at my nails and the surrounding skin, resulting in bleeding and discomfort.

I also had this thing where I could not step on lines or cracks in the pavement. If I did, anxiety would kick in, and I would be nervous the whole day as I waited for disaster to strike. Imagine not being able to walk "normal" for years, always having to look down and pay close attention to the pavement.

For a brief time, I also had a weird eating ritual where I would chew food a specific number of times and then spit it back out before eating it again. A part of my mind knew this was gross, but again, I couldn't help myself. If I didn’t do it, I feared something bad would happen.

As the years went by, and as I sought professional treatment, some of my obsessions and compulsions would wane or completely be gone, and new ones would develop. During therapy, I also learned that my OCD was tied to the stress and anxiety I experienced growing up (probably why I first developed nail picking, an anxiety coping mechanism).

You see, my father was a hoarder, an OCD subtype. He kept everything, and these items had to be kept and arranged a certain way. If something wasn't where it was supposed to be, it would upset him, and he would start raising his voice at us. So, as a child, I was constantly worried about touching and misplacing something.

My mother, I believe, had undiagnosed General Anxiety Disorder (GAD). She was always worried about something and was always expecting some catastrophe to happen. For example, even though our neighborhood was safe, she constantly worried someone might enter our house. Imagine living in a home where you were constantly told that something bad was about to happen.

Please note that I'm not sharing these stories because I blame or feel ill about my parents. My mom and dad were doing their best with what they had, and it's not their fault they were struggling with their own mental health problems.

As I look back on my childhood, there was also love in our home. However, there was also a constant atmosphere of chaos, stress, anxiety, and tension. I believe this is strongly part of why I was diagnosed with OCD and GAD as an adult.

Living with OCD and GAD is exhausting, so much so that, as an adult, I began to show symptoms of depression. So, in my mid-20s, I began to research possible treatments.

I underwent psychotherapy, specifically Cognitive Behavioral Therapy (CBT), and I was prescribed medication for my anxiety disorder. (This is because it was discovered during treatment that my anxiety disorder triggered my OCD.) As I learned and applied CBT techniques, I found "relief" for my OCD, so I'm very grateful for having undergone this therapy. After a few years, I discovered Dialectical Behavior Therapy (DBT), and the skills I learned with this treatment pushed me even further toward the life I wanted to live. This is why I am presenting these two therapies in this book. They both helped me become the well-adjusted adult I am today.

I still get anxiety attacks and experience OCD episodes occasionally, but they no longer cripple me. I've learned to live an abundant life with them because I have the skills to deal with life’s obstacles better. I earnestly hope you will accomplish the same with this book.

Who Should Read This Book

This book is primarily for people exhibiting symptoms or have been diagnosed with OCD. You might want to read this book to better understand what you're going through, or you might already be in therapy and want to use the exercises in this book as part of your treatment. If you've lived with OCD for years, this book can help you learn new ways to deal with your urges, compulsions, and other challenges.

This book is also for people who know someone struggling with OCD. One of the first things we can do to help and support someone we care about is to learn more about their situation. Understanding allows you to empathize, which people with OCD greatly appreciate.

Goals of This Book

This book aims to help people with OCD overcome their obsessions and compulsions and reclaim their lives by teaching them CBT and DBT skills. By working through this book, you will gain the confidence and resilience to confront obsessions, resist compulsions, manage anxiety, and lead a fulfilling life beyond the constraints of OCD. I hope this book is a valuable companion on your journey to overcoming OCD and achieving lasting recovery.

The CBT and DBT Exercises in This Book

This book will not cover every aspect of CBT and DBT because these therapies are extensive. I have deliberately chosen to highlight certain aspects of these therapies because these are, in my opinion, and experience, the most helpful for overcoming OCD.

Please also note that CBT and DBT are examples of "talk therapies." That is, they are meant to involve verbal communication between a licensed therapist and the individual seeking treatment. This is because therapies rely on active dialogue, discussion, and exploration of thoughts, emotions, behaviors, and experiences to facilitate change and promote psychological well-being. Therefore, self-help resources such as this book can be important supplementary tools.

Content Warning

This book contains content that may be triggering or distressing for individuals with OCD or related mental health conditions. It explores the nature of OCD, including its symptoms and underlying thought patterns, which may involve discussing intrusive thoughts, fears, and anxiety. It also addresses challenging behaviors associated with OCD, such as exposure to triggers and resisting compulsions. Important: please don't hesitate to ask for assistance or consult a specialist whenever you feel overwhelmed.

Be Kind to Yourself

Whenever I look back at my adolescent years, I feel a lot of empathy for myself and my family. I wish my parents had reached out and gotten the help they needed for their mental health problems for their own sake and our whole family.

As for my struggles with OCD, it's hard to express to others that horrible feeling I get whenever I can't "scratch that itch." For years, I felt like I had no control over my life. My OCD dictates my days, and that was that. Now, I know that is not true. Life doesn't just happen to me anymore. CBT and DBT have given me the tools to regain control of my life.

But I will be the first to say that healing is NOT a straightforward process. Your journey will have many ups and downs, so I advise you to be patient, compassionate, and understanding of yourself. Remember that every step you take, no matter how small, is a step towards progress.

About Me

---

*"I'm not saying I will heal you.
But I am sharing what healed me." – Barrett Huang*

My mental health journey inspired me to delve deeper into understanding the mind and its workings. This led me to pursue a bachelor's degree in psychology and complete Dr. Marsha Linehan's DBT Skills certificate program. Driven by the desire to "live a life worth living," I dedicated years to exploring happiness, philosophy, and personal growth.

I emphasize that this book draws primarily from my experiences with CBT and DBT and the stories shared by people who graciously allowed me to share their journeys with you. Through our collective experiences, we have found significant help and improvement with our OCD through these two therapies, enabling us to lead fulfilling and productive lives. We aim to pay it forward with gratitude by sharing our insights and experiences in this book.

Understanding OCD and Its Impact

"You lose time. You lose entire blocks of your day to obsessive thoughts or actions. I spend so much time finishing songs in my car before I can get out or redoing my entire shower routine because I lost count of how many times I scrubbed my left arm."
— Kelly Hill

What is OCD?

Obsessive-Compulsive Disorder, or OCD, is a mental health illness affecting a person's thinking and behaviour. Most people, when they hear of OCD, immediately have a visual of someone repeatedly doing something like hand washing or someone who needs to have things arranged in a particular way. However, that's just one *type* of this disorder. To fully understand OCD, let's first break it down into two components: obsessions and compulsions.

Obsessions are unwanted and intrusive thoughts, urges, or mental images that repeatedly enter a person's mind. These thoughts can be distressing and cause anxiety or fear. They are often difficult to control or ignore. Examples of obsessions include worrying about germs and cleanliness, fearing harm to oneself or others, or having intrusive thoughts about symmetry or order.

Compulsions are repeated actions or thoughts people feel compelled to do because of obsessions. These behaviors are intended to reduce the anxiety or distress caused by the obsessions. Compulsions are often rigid and can become rituals. Examples of compulsions include excessive handwashing, checking locks repeatedly, arranging items in a specific order, or counting to a certain number.

So, obsessions are unwanted thoughts or images that intrude into a person's mind, causing anxiety and discomfort. To cope with this anxiety and discomfort, individuals with OCD engage in repetitive behaviors or mental acts to get some relief. In short, obsessions lead to compulsions. But that's not always the case.

The presence of compulsions is not a requirement for an OCD diagnosis. In some cases of OCD, individuals may experience obsessions primarily without engaging in visible or noticeable compulsive behaviors. These are called "pure obsessional" or "primarily obsessional" OCD. However, despite no visible compulsions, the distressing and intrusive nature of the obsessions can still significantly impact a person's daily life and cause significant distress.

Content Warning: harmful thoughts, self-harm, suicide.

One of my obsessions as an adult had something to do with knives. I often wondered what would happen if I stabbed myself with a cutting knife. Would it be a sharp pain, or would it take a few seconds before I felt the full painful impact of what I had done? Would I bleed out? If I did, would I die slowly or quickly? Would I survive?

At one point, I lived in a condo on the 17th floor. I became obsessed with what would happen if I jumped off the balcony. Would I break some bones or die instantly? Would I be able to walk or become paralyzed? What would my last thoughts be before hitting the pavement? How would my family react? Would anyone even care? Hey, maybe it would end all of my suffering.

I would often get these thoughts, but I've never taken action. Many people with OCD know such thoughts are irrational and harmful, so they wouldn't do anything about it or act it out. However, once these UNWANTED thoughts enter our minds, we can't stop thinking about them repeatedly.

So, even though I never acted on these harmful thoughts, they still brought me significant distress, interfered with my daily functioning, and consumed a significant amount of my time and energy.

What are the Causes of OCD?

Researchers believe that OCD is a combination of different factors. The following are some of the widely considered potential causes of this mental health disorder:

1.) **Biological Factors**: There is evidence to suggest that there may be a genetic component to OCD.[1,2] It can run in families; certain genes may contribute to a person's vulnerability to developing OCD. Additionally, there may be differences in brain structure and function, specifically involving the areas responsible for regulating anxiety and controlling repetitive behaviors.

2.) **Environmental Factors**: Certain environmental factors, such as stressful life events, trauma, or significant changes in life circumstances, may trigger OCD symptoms in some individuals.[3,4] These factors can interact with genetic predispositions, influencing the development of OCD.

3.) **Chemical Imbalance**: Some research suggests that imbalances in certain chemicals in the brain, such as serotonin, may play a role in the development of OCD.[5,6] Serotonin is a neurotransmitter that helps regulate mood, anxiety, and behavior.

4.) **Cognitive Factors**: Certain thinking patterns may contribute to developing or maintaining OCD symptoms.[7,8] For example, individuals with OCD may have exaggerated beliefs about the importance of their thoughts or the need to prevent specific outcomes, leading to heightened anxiety and compulsive behaviors.

Please keep in mind that these are simplified explanations. The reasons for OCD can be complicated and different for each person. The interaction of genetic, environmental, brain chemical, and neurological variables all likely contributes to the development and manifestation of OCD.

What are the Different Types of OCD?

One of the things confusing about OCD is the terminologies used. Some label the list below as "types"; others call them "subtypes." Others list four types/subtypes, while others list eight. I guess things change as more becomes known about this disorder. As of this writing, the list below itemizes what is widely considered as the different types of OCD.

1.) **Contamination OCD**: People with contamination OCD fear germs, dirt, or contaminants. They may excessively wash their hands or clean their surroundings to reduce anxiety and prevent illness.

2.) **Checking OCD**: This type involves a constant need to check things repeatedly. For example, individuals may repeatedly check if doors are locked, appliances are turned off, or if they've made mistakes.

3.) **Symmetry and Ordering OCD**: People with this type of OCD have a strong urge for things to be arranged in a specific order or pattern. They may spend excessive time arranging objects, aligning items symmetrically, or ensuring perfect order.

4.) **Hoarding OCD**: Hoarding OCD involves intense difficulty letting go of possessions, leading to excessive clutter and difficulty organizing spaces.

People with hoarding OCD may feel extreme distress when trying to discard items.

5.) **Intrusive Thoughts OCD**: This type involves distressing and unwanted thoughts or mental images that are often violent, sexual, or blasphemous in nature. Individuals may try to suppress or neutralize these thoughts through mental rituals or repetitive behaviors.

6.) **Just-Right OCD**: This type revolves around a feeling of incompleteness or discomfort until certain tasks or routines are done "just right." For instance, someone may repeatedly adjust items until they feel they are in perfect alignment.

From the list above, I suffered from Checking, Intrusive Thoughts, and Just-Right OCD. (My father has Hoarding OCD.) So, know that OCD types are not mutually exclusive, and you may show symptoms of one or a combination of different OCD types at any time.

If you haven't been diagnosed with OCD but are experiencing its symptoms, you might want to take the ***OCD Symptoms Checklist*** *on page 159 or the* ***OCD Self-Assessment Quiz*** *on page 162.*

Do you Know What Triggers Your OCD?

A "trigger" refers to something that sets off a reaction or response. It's like pressing a button that starts a particular action or emotion. In terms of OCD, a "trigger" can be a person, place, or situation that can set off or worsen OCD symptoms.

Triggers can vary from person to person, but they often fall into a few common categories:

1.) **Obsessive Triggers** are thoughts, images, or worries that repeatedly come to mind and cause distress. Examples include concerns about germs or contamination, fears of harm coming to oneself or others, worries about making mistakes, or intrusive thoughts of a taboo nature.

2.) **Environmental Triggers** are certain environments or situations that prompt OCD symptoms. Examples include being in a messy or disorganized space, being in situations that deviate from your sense of order or symmetry, or where you need to perform certain rituals or checks to prevent harm.

3.) **Interpersonal Triggers** are frequently associated with the people around you and your interaction with them. Examples include receiving criticism or judgment, feeling pressured, experiencing conflict or misunderstanding, or hearing or witnessing another person's stress or trauma. Although not common, positive interactions may trigger OCD as well. For example, an anniversary dinner may suddenly trigger fears about happiness not lasting.

4.) **Emotional Triggers** are strong emotions such as anxiety, stress, or fear. For instance, when you feel overwhelmed, you may engage in compulsive behaviors or rituals to alleviate the distress.

5.) **Life Events or Transitions** are significant events, changes, or transitions that can cause OCD symptoms. Examples include starting a new job, moving to a new place, going through relationship changes, or experiencing loss or trauma.

OCD triggers are unique to each individual. Additionally, triggers can change or evolve as your OCD symptoms change. Identifying your triggers is crucial in managing and treating your OCD because it allows you to develop strategies to cope with and respond to triggering situations healthier. If you're unaware of what sets off your OCD, you might want to take the ***Know your OCD Triggers*** exercise on page 166.

The Cycle of Obsessions and Compulsions

A person with OCD experiences **unwanted thoughts or images** (obsessions). These trigger **strong emotional responses** (e.g., anxiety, fear, guilt, disgust, etc.) and result in **certain behaviors or actions** (compulsions).

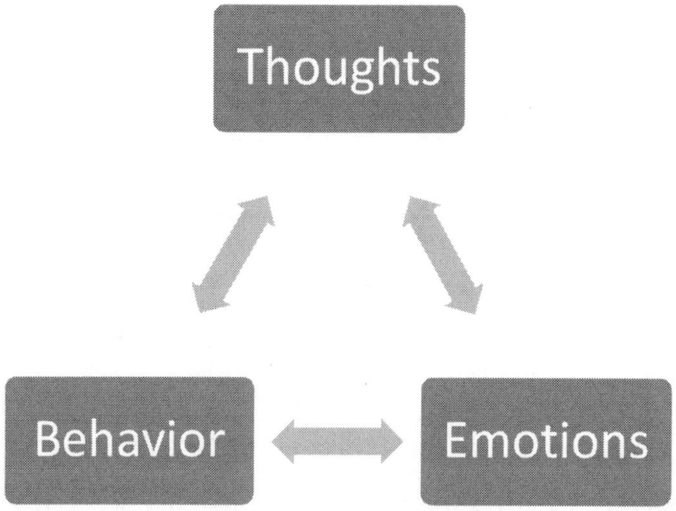

Now, thoughts, emotions, and behavior are interconnected in everyone. However, people with OCD experience these different components of human experience and functioning negatively and get caught in a continuous loop (a.k.a. the OCD cycle), where obsessions trigger anxiety, compulsions provide temporary relief, and this relief reinforces the habits, *maintaining* the cycle.

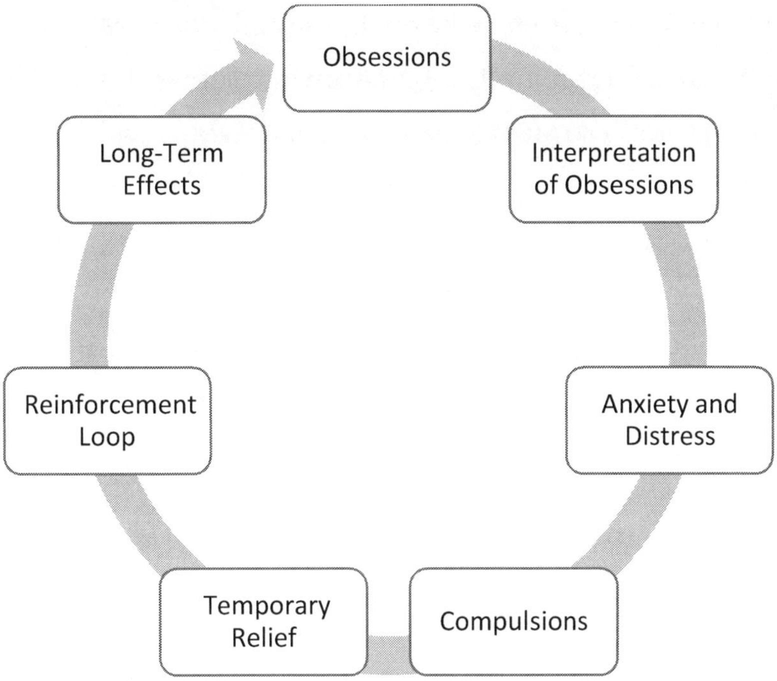

1.) **Obsessions**: People with OCD experience unwanted, intrusive, and distressing thoughts or urges that keep returning to their minds. These thoughts are often irrational or unrealistic, creating intense anxiety or discomfort.

2.) **Interpretation of Obsessions**: Individuals with OCD tend to interpret these obsessions exaggeratedly or catastrophically. You may believe that the thoughts signify something terrible or that you are in danger. In my case, if I didn't go through my morning poster ritual before school, I truly believed that something bad would happen or that I would never experience that "okay" feeling again.

3.) **Anxiety and Distress**: The obsessions trigger anxiety and distress, making you feel highly anxious, uncomfortable, or overwhelmed. As such, you feel a need to do something to relieve the anxiety you're feeling.

4.) **Compulsions**: In response to the anxiety and distress, you may engage in compulsions, which are repetitive behaviors or mental acts you feel compelled to perform to reduce the anxiety or prevent something bad from happening.

5.) **Temporary Relief**: When you perform a compulsion, it temporarily relieves the anxiety and distress caused by your obsessions. It gives you a sense of control and reduces your anxiety. The fact that relief is short-term is not something you focus on. You just want relief from all the anxiety and distress!

6.) **Reinforcement Loop**: The relief you feel from performing the compulsion reinforces the connection between the obsession and the compulsion in your mind. This creates a vicious cycle where the obsession keeps returning, leading to more compulsive behaviors.

7.) **Long-Term Effects**: Over time, you become stuck in this cycle of obsessions and compulsions, which can significantly interfere with your daily life, relationships, and well-being. Because the relief you get from compulsions is short-lived, you must continue performing them.

OCD is a vicious, self-perpetuating cycle, creating a challenging loop that requires intervention to break free. The key lies in altering, modifying, or "hijacking" specific elements within this loop. The following chapters will explore effective strategies to achieve this goal.

Common Misconceptions about OCD

It's important to learn the common misconceptions about OCD to prevent misunderstanding and stigma. Here are some of the most prevalent misconceptions:

1.) **OCD is about being a "neat freak" (being excessively clean or organized).** While some individuals with OCD may have obsessions and compulsions related to neatness and order, others have obsessions and compulsions unrelated to cleanliness or organization. OCD can manifest in a wide range of themes.

2.) **OCD is a personality quirk or a character flaw.** This is incredibly false. OCD is a recognized mental health disorder with biological and psychological origins. It's not something that individuals can snap out of or control with willpower.

3.) **Everyone has a little bit of OCD**. While it is common for people to have certain preferences, routines, or occasional repetitive behaviors, having some quirks or habits does not equate to having OCD. This disorder involves significant distress, interference with daily life and significantly impacts an individual's well-being. I find that this particular misconception trivializes this disorder, which is a disservice to anyone with OCD.

4.) **OCD is rare**. OCD is actually more common than many people realize. According to the Anxiety and Depression Association of America, about 2.3% of Americans have OCD.[9] Worldwide, OCD prevalence is believed to be between 1% and 2%.[10] This number is likely even higher because OCD, like many mental health disorders, is often underreported.[11]

5.) **OCD is not real. People who claim they have OCD just don't have willpower.** It is tough for people without OCD to understand our internal struggles. I've lost count of how often I've received comments such as "just don't do it" or "oh, don't give in to your compulsions then."

People don't understand that avoiding triggers or stopping compulsions without appropriate treatment is often ineffective in managing OCD. Effective treatment typically involves specialized therapy, such as those provided in DBT and CBT.

The Emotional and Functional Impact of OCD

Unsurprisingly, OCD can have a significant emotional and functional impact on your everyday life. It affects your thoughts, emotions, behaviors, and overall well-being.

1.) **Anxiety and Distress**: OCD's persistent and intrusive nature can cause intense anxiety and distress in your life because these unwanted thoughts lead to a constant state of worry, fear, and unease.

2.) **Impaired Quality of Life**: OCD can get in the way of your school, work, relationships, and social activities, among other things. Because compulsions and obsessions take up a lot of time, they can make it hard for people to do important things, reach their goals, or enjoy their free time.

3.) **Problems with Daily Functioning**: OCD can make doing things well and quickly difficult. Actually, never mind "quickly," OCD can make it difficult to get normal, everyday tasks done at all. Compulsions can take up a lot of time and energy, affecting how you perform normal activities like showering, getting to work, cooking, etc.

4.) **Social and Interpersonal Impact**: OCD can strain relationships and social interactions. You may feel embarrassed, ashamed, or misunderstood due to the nature of your obsessions and compulsions. You may even try to hide your symptoms, leading to social withdrawal or avoidance of situations that trigger your anxiety. This can lead to feelings of isolation and difficulties in forming or maintaining relationships.

Content Warning: the following story contains distressing material.

This is what Agnes*, a reader, had to say: "*I don't know how it started. I really don't. All I remember is that I absolutely FEARED my 20th birthday. I remember dreading leaving my teen years. I felt I didn't make the most of my childhood, and now I had to leave it? Plus, all that unknown and all that uncertainty kept me up at night. What if I make mistakes? What if I mess up my adult years too? What if I couldn't deal with "adult" things? I couldn't see myself beyond being 19. I didn't want to be an adult. I felt resentful and anxious, and I began to have self-harming thoughts.*

This obsession turned into a compulsion to avoid any and all pregnant women. I didn't even like seeing them on TV. Pregnant women brought out insane jealousy in me. Here is someone with a baby just about to start their childhood while mine was wasted and gone.

I felt ashamed about my behavior, so I hid it and hid it well. And that meant avoiding people. I started to withdraw socially. I wouldn't answer my friend's calls and refused to go out. My mom noticed my changes, and I'm grateful she made a big effort to convince me to seek counseling, where I learned CBT techniques.

I'm not "cured." I'm still uncomfortable around pregnant women, but I go out now. I'm even seeing someone. I also reached my 20th birthday without hurting myself, which is the biggest plus for me and my family.

---

* *Name changed for privacy.*

5.) **Emotional Toll**: OCD can take a huge emotional toll on you. The constant battle with intrusive thoughts, the need to perform compulsions, and the fear of being unable to control these thoughts and behaviors can lead to frustration, guilt, and low self-esteem. As such, depression and anxiety disorders commonly co-occur with OCD due to the chronic stress and emotional burden it imposes. Note: According to some research, approximately 76% of people with OCD have an anxiety disorder such as General Anxiety Disorder (GAD), Post-Traumatic Stress Disorder (PTSD), panic disorder, and others.[12]

6.) **Effects on Decision-Making**: Obsessions and compulsions can significantly influence your decision-making process. You may struggle with making choices or decisions due to excessive doubts, fear of making mistakes, or concerns about the consequences of your actions. This can further impair your ability to navigate daily life and achieve personal goals.

It's important to note that the impact of OCD varies from person to person. However, the result is that OCD negatively affects nearly everything about you and around you.

In the next chapter, we'll dive into an overview of two powerful therapeutic approaches: Dialectical Behavior Therapy (DBT) and Cognitive-Behavioral Therapy (CBT).

DBT and CBT are evidence-based treatments that have shown great effectiveness in addressing OCD. By combining the strengths of these two therapies, you can create a powerful framework for managing OCD symptoms, enhancing emotional well-being, and fostering personal growth. Let's get started!

Overview of Cognitive-Behavioral Therapy (CBT) and Dialectical Behavior Therapy (DBT)

Do you remember the OCD cycle?

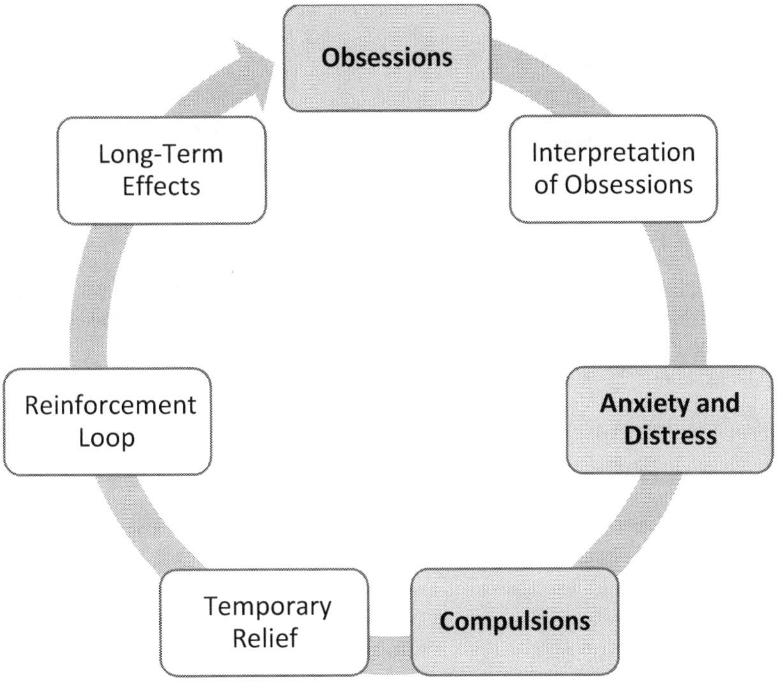

Breaking this cycle is a key objective of OCD treatment.

To this end, Cognitive-Behavioral Therapy (CBT) and Dialectical Behavior Therapy (DBT) are considered effective because they both address the interconnection of **obsessions** (thoughts), **anxiety and distress** (emotions), and **compulsions** (behavior).

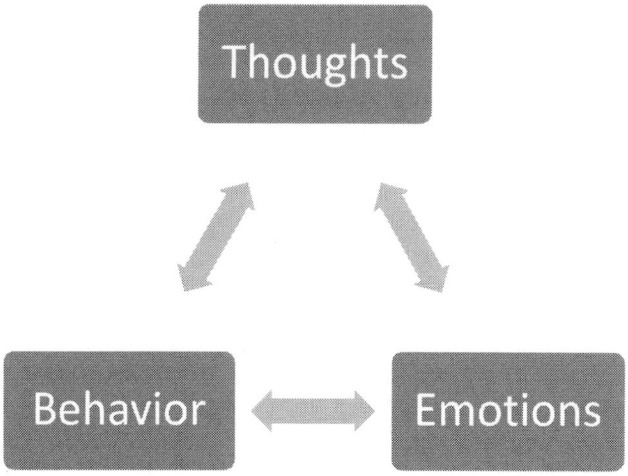

CBT has its roots in *behaviorism*, a psychological approach popular in the early 1900s. Behaviorism focuses on studying observable behaviors. The belief is that one can change behavior by monitoring, understanding, and measuring it. Influential figures in this field include Ivan Pavlov, John B. Watson, and B.F. Skinner laid the groundwork for understanding how behavior can be shaped through *conditioning*. (Focus: behavioral change.)

In the 1950s and 1960s, psychologists like Albert Ellis and Aaron Beck started to look into how thoughts and ideas affect emotions and behavior. Ellis created Rational Emotive Behavior Therapy (REBT). Its main goal was to challenge irrational thoughts and replace them with more reasonable ones. Beck then came up with Cognitive Therapy. This therapy's main focus was finding and changing negative thought habits. (Focus: cognitive restructuring.)

In the 1970s, behaviorism and cognitive techniques finally came together, leading to the development of what we know today as Cognitive Behavioral Therapy or CBT. This integration showed how thoughts, emotions, and behavior are connected and how important it is to work on all three for effective therapy.

Over the next few decades, CBT became known and supported as an evidence-based therapy for various mental health problems, such as depression, anxiety, OCD, eating disorders, and other mental health issues.

CBT also started to evolve and expand beyond its original applications. Variations of CBT were developed to address specific issues, such as Dialectical Behavior Therapy (DBT) for borderline personality disorder (BPD).

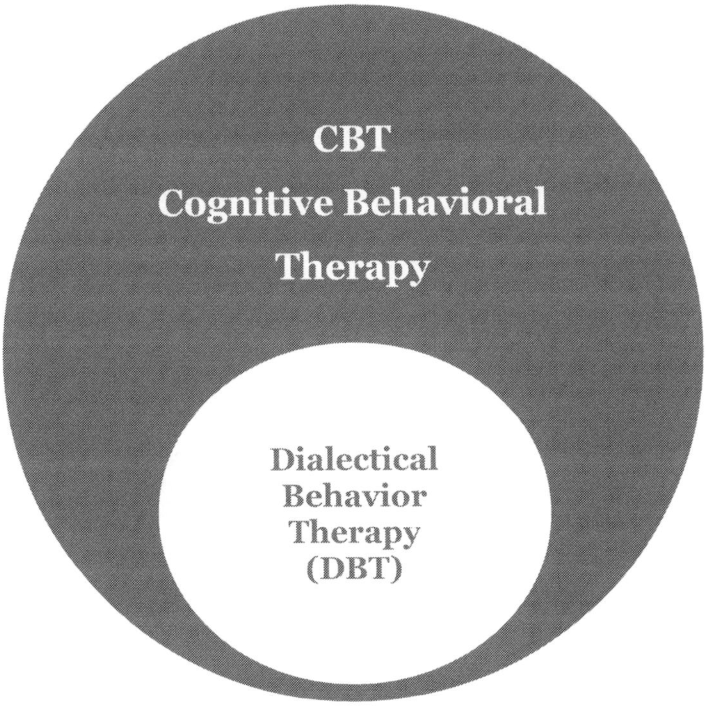

DBT was developed by Dr. Marsha M. Linehan[13] in the 1980s due to her and her colleagues' work with individuals suffering from BPD. (It's also worth noting that Dr. Linehan suffered from BPD in her teens.[14])

When DBT was introduced, it was considered groundbreaking because it was the first treatment to combine Eastern mindfulness practices and Western psychological techniques, creating a unique and integrative approach to therapy. Due to its effectiveness, DBT has evolved through the years, becoming known and supported as an evidence-based therapy for BPD and other mental health disorders, including OCD.

CBT and DBT address the **thoughts**, **emotions**, and **behavior** triangle, albeit slightly differently.

In CBT, the focus is primarily on *cognitive restructuring* (questioning the irrational ways of thinking linked to OCD) and *behavioral change* (modifying the ways one reacts to obsessions).

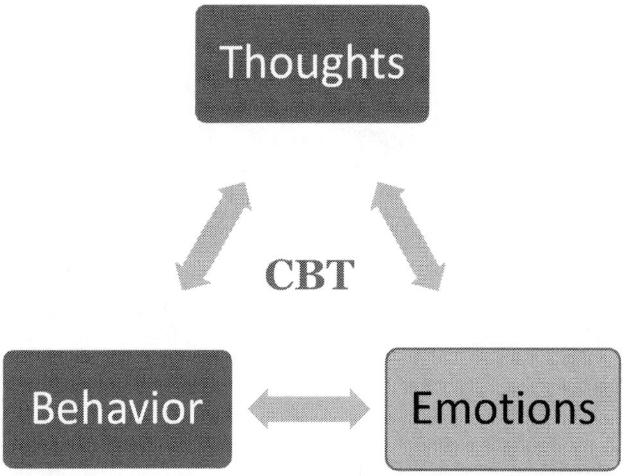

In DBT, the focus is primarily on *distress tolerance* and *emotion regulation.* In relation to OCD, DBT aims to address the anxiety and distress caused by unwanted thoughts, thereby preventing corresponding compulsive behaviors from occurring.

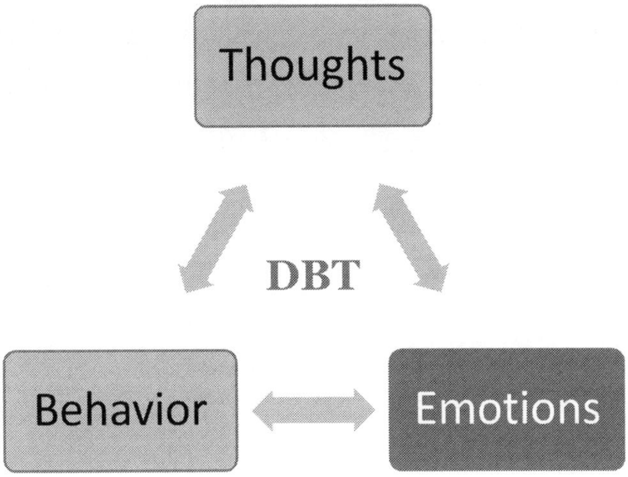

Due to CBT's emphasis on changing unwanted thoughts (obsessions) and resulting behaviors (compulsions), it's considered more effective when it comes to OCD treatment[15,16]. So, you might wonder, why include DBT in this book if CBT is more effective?

Recent research shows that DBT is also effective in OCD treatment.[17,18] It's one of the treatments considered "third-wave CBT."[19]

Third-wave CBT treatments focus on changing negative thoughts and behaviors and accepting AND understanding emotions more compassionately. That is, instead of trying to fight against distressing emotions, third-wave CBT teaches individuals to observe and accept their feelings non-judgmentally. This can help people develop healthier coping strategies and a greater sense of well-being.

In my opinion, CBT and DBT are a "power combo" when treating OCD. This is why I put these two treatments together in this book.

Even though CBT was developed first, the next chapter will focus on DBT. I've decided to present DBT first because I believe that it provides a strong foundation and better preparation for adopting CBT. Skills such as acceptance, non-judgment of emotions, mindfulness, etc., can significantly enhance your ability to grasp and apply CBT techniques effectively. However, I will keep the discussion of DBT brief, providing you with the basics, before delving into CBT in more detail later.

Overcoming OCD Using DBT Techniques

"DBT saved my life. It helped me break free from self-destructive behaviors and develop healthier coping strategies."
– Debbie Corso

DBT Core Principles: Acceptance and Change

DBT applies the concept of *dialectics*, which is a way of thinking and solving problems using opposing or contradictory viewpoints. In this case, it applies two seemingly opposing principles: Acceptance and Change.

Dr. Linehan believes that the first step to mental healing is to accept your present reality AS IS. No denying, ignoring, or fighting that you're suffering from OCD. Just complete acknowledgment that you have it. In DBT, this is called Radical Acceptance.

Radical Acceptance is when you fully and totally accept reality as it is without judging or fighting it. It's accepting things we can't change and giving up trying to control or fight reality. Radical Acceptance is necessary because we can't change something we don't accept, right?

You may think, *"If I accept I have OCD, why should I still change? Doesn't accepting mean approval? Doesn't it mean surrendering to my OCD and letting it run my life?"* No, it doesn't.

Acceptance is not agreeing, approving, or giving in to OCD. You're just accepting the reality that you have it. Furthermore, you're not accepting and changing the same thing.

What you're accepting -> the reality you have OCD.
What you're changing -> how you handle your OCD.

And why do you want to change how you deal with your OCD? Because the way things are for you today is not working for you. You are suffering, and something inside you knows life can be better. In DBT, "better" comes after change, which refers to developing new skills and behaviors to feel better and improve your current situation.

Let's consider this: say you don't accept you have OCD. Will this denial make your OCD disappear? Will your life get better? Unfortunately, the answer is most likely no. By denying the reality of your condition, you risk perpetuating the cycle of obsessions and compulsions. Without acknowledging your OCD, each day may feel heavier than the last as the symptoms persist and potentially intensify.

But what if you accept that you're suffering from OCD? Now, you can move on. Now, you can start figuring out how to manage and overcome it!

I'm not going to lie. Acceptance and Change are not easy principles to apply. But I have discovered that it can be extremely freeing once you open up to these concepts.

If you're still unsure, I have lined up the following worksheets to help you understand and adopt the principles of Acceptance and Change in your life.

Worksheet: Radical Acceptance

Radical Acceptance = Reality Acceptance. In the circle below, please write your reality right now. Simply jot down whatever comes to mind. Remember that all of your feelings and experiences are valid.

Examples: (1) I'm so tired. (2) I'm afraid. (3) I'm ashamed of my thoughts. (4) I feel like I have no control whatsoever. (5) I can't say "no" to my own mind.

Worksheet: Desire to Change

Start conditioning your mind for change by writing down a few thoughts about how change can benefit you. Don't think too much about this. Just write whatever comes to mind in the circle below. Here's a prompt to help you: *If I can manage my OCD better, I might...*

Examples: (1) Experience calmness. (2) Accomplish more in 24 hours. (2) Have more meaningful relationships. (4) Sleep better! (5) Have time for self-care.

DBT Primary Skills

DBT comprises four core skills: Mindfulness, Distress Tolerance, Emotion Regulation, and Interpersonal Effectiveness.

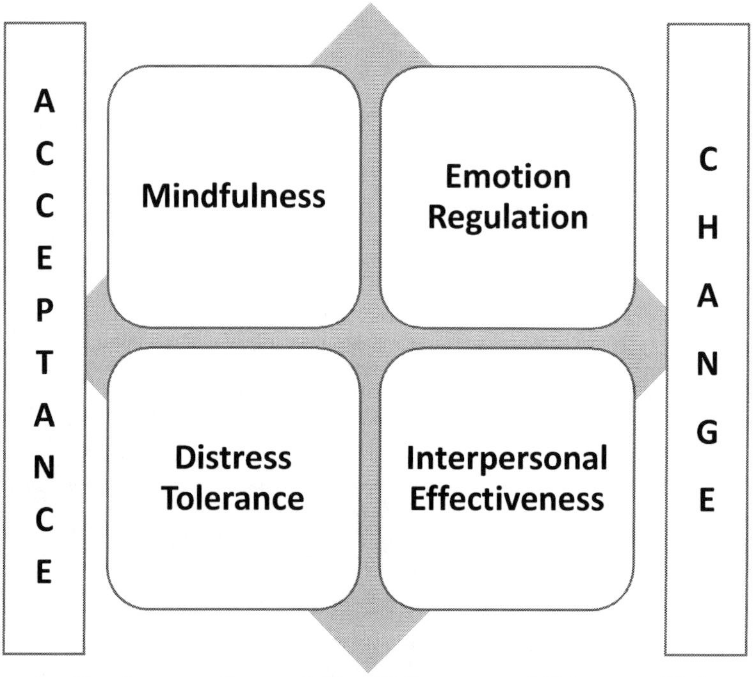

As you can see in the image above, Mindfulness and Distress Tolerance skills help with Acceptance, while Emotion Regulation and Interpersonal Effectiveness help with Change.

Mindfulness

Mindfulness is being 100% present in the moment, fully aware of your surroundings, thoughts, and feelings. It means giving all your attention to what's happening around and inside you without judgment. It's the practice of fully living in the present. You are neither in the past nor the future. You're just in NOW.

Mindfulness is important because it will help you observe your thoughts and emotions without getting caught up in them. I always like to think of mindfulness as a "mental pause." It's like deliberately slowing down your mind to observe what's happening.

For example, say there's a big backyard BBQ party going on. A person who's not mindful might take the whole scenario as one big, noisy, overwhelming blur. On the other hand, a mindful person has the skill to slow down, be quiet inside, look around, observe, and absorb.

Suddenly, the loud music is not "noise"; it contributes to the party's overall fun and laid-back atmosphere. Kids are not just running around creating chaos; you notice how absorbed they are in a specific game. You look at the abundance of food and drinks and realize the magnitude of the host's preparation to pull the party off. This, in turn, makes you appreciate being invited to the BBQ party in the first place. You're not overwhelmed anymore; you're grateful and ready to participate and have fun.

Notice in the example above that by practicing mindfulness, one cannot only reign in unpleasant thoughts and emotions. It can also turn things around and make you feel better. Yes, mindfulness has that power!

If you really think about it, mindfulness is the ability to control oneself because it involves intentionally directing your attention to the present moment without judgment or attachment to thoughts or emotions.

In relation to OCD, mindfulness can help you observe yourself objectively and, perhaps more importantly, *non-reactively*. This awareness lets you choose how you respond to internal and external stimuli. Rather than automatically reacting to OCD triggers, mindfulness enables you to pause and consciously choose your response.

Worksheet: Belly Breathing

One of the most effective methods to be "in the moment" is to begin paying attention to how you breathe. So let's start with some basic abdominal breathing.

Belly Breathing, or diaphragmatic breathing, is a technique that promotes relaxation and stress reduction. The following are the steps for belly breathing:

1. Take a seat or lie down on your bed.
2. Place one hand on your tummy and one on your chest.
3. Gently inhale through your nose, allowing your stomach to expand like a balloon. (Your chest should be quite motionless.)
4. Slowly exhale through your lips, allowing your belly to shrink like a balloon. (Try to expel all of the air from your lungs.)
5. Continue to breathe in this manner, focusing on the sensation of your abdomen rising and falling with each breath, like gentle ocean waves.

Make sure you're breathing deeply from your diaphragm, not shallowly from your chest. Try this technique with closed eyes, imagining a serene picture, or repeating a calming mantra to increase relaxation. As you become more familiar with the method, gradually lengthen your belly breaths.

Worksheet: Square Breathing

Square Breathing, or box breathing, is a bit more advanced than belly breathing because there's a bit more structure to it. Here's how it goes:

1. Find a comfortable position. You can sit down or lie down. If you're away from home, find a quiet place to stand undisturbed comfortably.
2. Close your eyes and take a few deep breaths to relax your body. Let go of any tension.
3. **Inhale** through your nose to the count of four. Feel your breath filling your lungs and expanding your abdomen. Focus your attention solely on the sensation of the breath entering your body.
4. **Hold** your breath to the count of four. Keep your lungs comfortably filled with air during this hold without straining or feeling any discomfort.
5. **Exhale** through your mouth for a count of four, releasing the breath gradually and completely. As you exhale, imagine any tension or stress leaving your body.
6. **Hold** your breath for four counts before starting the next inhale.

Remember to adapt the technique to your comfort level. If counting to four feels too long or short, adjust the count to a pace that suits you. Square breathing can be done anywhere and anytime, providing a portable tool for awareness, relaxation, and stress management.

Worksheet: Mindful Body Scan

This exercise helps you cultivate awareness and presence in your body. It can shift your focus away from obsessive thoughts by redirecting your attention to the present moment by making you pay attention to how your body feels. Also, OCD can lead to physical tension and discomfort due to heightened anxiety and compulsive behaviors. This exercise will help you become aware of areas of tension in your body, enabling you to release physical stress and relax consciously.

Follow these step-by-step instructions:

1. Sit or lie down in a comfortable position. Close your eyes if you want to. Take a few deep breaths to relax and settle into the present moment.
2. Begin by bringing your attention to your breath. Feel the natural rhythm of your breath as you inhale and exhale. Notice the sensation of the breath as it moves in and out of your body.
3. Shift your focus to your feet. Pay attention to any sensations in your feet. Are they warm or cool? Do you feel any tension or relaxation in this area? Simply observe without judgment.
4. Gradually shift your awareness to your lower legs and calves. Notice any sensations, such as warmth, tingling, or heaviness. Allow yourself to be fully present with whatever you experience.
5. Slowly move your attention to your knees and thighs. Observe any sensations or feelings in this part of your body. Be aware of the connection your body has with the surface beneath you.
6. Next, gently shift your focus to your hips and pelvis. Feel the weight of your body in this area and any sensations that arise. Take your time and explore the present moment with curiosity.

7. Gradually direct your attention to your abdomen and lower back. Notice the rise and fall of your breath in this area. If you encounter any tension, breathe into that space to release it.
8. Shift your awareness to your chest and upper back. Feel the expansion and contraction of your ribcage with each breath. Allow any feelings or sensations to be present without resistance.
9. Slowly move your focus to your shoulders, arms, and hands. Notice any sensations, tension, or relaxation in these areas. Be fully present with the experience at the moment.
10. Gradually bring your attention to your neck and head. Notice any sensations, such as stiffness or ease, in this part of your body. Allow your face and scalp to relax.
11. Now, expand your awareness to your entire body. Feel the sensations of your body as a whole, resting in the present moment. Embrace a sense of unity and presence with your body.
12. When you are ready to conclude the exercise, take a few deep breaths and gently open your eyes if they were closed. Take a moment to notice how you feel after this exercise.

Distress Tolerance

Distress Tolerance is all about *crisis survival.* In terms of OCD, it is learning how to "ride out" the urge to act out a compulsion. How is this helpful? I believe that we are all stronger than we think we are.

Looking back, I sometimes did my morning Emma Bunton poster ritual for HOURS because I was anxious and afraid of what *might* happen the rest of the day if I didn't do it. So the ritual addressed my anxiety over some future potential harm or disaster. But I never thought I should try and ride out my anxiety instead. I never thought that maybe, just maybe, I could live to the fullest despite anxiety's presence.

So, Distress Tolerance is learning how best to live with anxiety and other unpleasant emotions (due to an obsession) rather than trying to chase distressing feelings away by performing a compulsion.

If you're concerned that you won't be able to withstand being in a prolonged state of anxiousness, fear, or distress, remember that the more you can tolerate such difficult circumstances, the higher your resilience will be!

Here are some additional thoughts for you:

- Fear is necessary to grow your courage.
- Struggles develop your strengths.
- Be brave, but always be kind and patient with yourself too.

A Note about Avoidance Behavior

Distress Tolerance is NOT about avoidance. The following exercises are designed to help you *cope with distressing emotions and situations as they are happening*. By learning to tolerate and accept discomfort, you can prevent yourself from resorting to harmful or impulsive behaviors. However, if these exercises are misused or overused, they may inadvertently promote the development of avoidance behavior.

So, please remember that it's important to acknowledge and process the thoughts and emotions surrounding OCD. Distress Tolerance is about surviving anxiety and distress, not avoiding what triggers them. (For more information about Avoidance Behavior, please see page 114.)

Tip: Before attempting Distress Tolerance exercises, it's best to be comfortable with Mindfulness first.

Worksheet: Urge Surfing

There is no single emotion in this world that lasts forever. So this exercise is to help you practice observing and "riding out" urges to engage in compulsive behaviors.

1. Do some breathing exercises to relax your body and center yourself.
2. Choose a specific compulsive behavior or urge related to your OCD that you commonly experience.

My specific compulsive behavior (urge) is:

Examples:

I have a compulsion to wash my hands excessively.

I have a compulsion to check things repeatedly.

____

____

____

3. Find a comfortable and quiet space to sit or lie down without distractions.
4. Close your eyes, take a deep breath, and focus on the sensations of your breath as it enters and leaves your body. Allow yourself to relax and become present in the moment.
5. Bring your chosen compulsion or urge into your awareness without judgment. **Visualize it as a wave** rising within you.
6. Observe the physical sensations, thoughts, and emotions that arise as you focus on the compulsion or urge. Notice *where* in your body you feel the urge most strongly. For instance, a compulsion to wash your hands excessively may provoke a feeling of heaviness or even an itch on your hands.
7. Begin to **view the urge as a wave that rises and falls**. Picture yourself on a surfboard, riding the wave rather than being consumed by it. Allow the wave to peak and begin to subside naturally.

8. Remind yourself that waves eventually retreat, and so will the urge. **Practice accepting the presence of the urge without acting on the compulsion.**
9. Maintain your focus on the present moment, bringing your attention back to your breath whenever your mind wanders or the urge feels overwhelming. **Use your breath as an anchor** to stay grounded.
10. Notice any changes in the intensity of the urge as you continue to observe it without giving in to the compulsion. **Recognize that urges, like waves, naturally fluctuate and diminish over time.**
11. **Stay committed to "surfing" the urge**, allowing it to rise and fall without acting on the compulsion. Remind yourself that by doing so, you are building distress tolerance and challenging the power of the urge.
12. Gradually increase the duration of each urge surfing session, challenging yourself to tolerate the urge for longer periods.
13. After completing the exercise, take a few moments to reflect on your experience. Notice any insights or changes in your relationship with the compulsion or urge.

Urge Surfing takes practice and persistence, so please don't be frustrated if you give in to your compulsion the first time you try this exercise. Remember, always direct patience and compassion to yourself.

Worksheet: STOP

STOP is a great DBT exercise that can *interrupt* the automatic and impulsive reactions often accompanying OCD. It will help you develop the skill of gaining control of your emotions and avoiding acting on them.

S	**Stop.** Stop! Freeze in place and don't move at all. Do this each time you experience an intrusive thought or urge to engage in a compulsion. Doing this encourages you to pause and become aware of the obsessive thought or the urge without acting on it immediately. This moment of stopping creates a much-needed space for mindfulness and self-awareness. For example, say you feel the need to check if the door is locked even though you know you just did it a few minutes ago. Instead of getting up and doing so, STOP. Freeze yourself in your current position.
T	**Take a step back.** After stopping, take a mental step back and take a breath. Focus on your breathing to anchor your attention to the present moment, promoting relaxation and reducing the intensity of anxiety associated with your OCD thoughts or urges.

How did you take a step back?

Example: I did Mindful Body Scan, page 43.

O

Observe.

Mindfully observe the specific details of your obsessive thought or compulsive urge *without judgment*. This awareness fosters a more objective perspective on your thoughts and emotions, reducing their power over you!

Just observe without judgment, tolerate the moment, and re-direct as needed until you feel the urge to give in to any compulsion dissipate.

How did you mindfully observe?

Example:

(1) Ok, I'm having the thought that I need to check if the door is locked.
(2) I'm feeling anxious. I can feel it on my chest.
(3) I'm going to Square Breathe.
(4) With each deep breath, the pressure on my chest seems to be easing.
(5) I'm just going to let this thought come and go.

Proceed mindfully.

This step involves deciding how to respond to your obsessive thought or urge more intentionally. Instead of acting on the compulsion automatically, make a conscious choice to delay or resist the compulsive behavior. By proceeding mindfully, you challenge OCD's grip on your actions and develop healthier coping strategies.

P

What did you do to proceed mindfully?

Example: I went up to the attic, where I had some gym equipment, and engaged in some rigorous Zumba dancing.

Worksheet: TIPP

TIPP skills assist you in tolerating distress by regulating your body's chemistry. Studies indicate that modifying your physical state can also positively influence your mental and emotional well-being.[20,21]

T	**Temperature.** Temperature can help in the regulation of emotional intensity. Plunging your face into cold water, applying a cold compress to your forehead, or pouring cold water on your wrists might cause a physical shock response that disturbs acute emotional arousal for a short period. This is especially useful when dealing with extreme anxiety or intrusive thoughts associated with OCD.
I	**Intense Exercise.** Engaging in intense physical activities, such as running or vigorous activity, releases *endorphins*, which are natural mood elevators. These endorphins can counteract the distress associated with OCD obsessions and compulsions, providing a sense of relief and improved emotional well-being. Also, have you ever noticed that you have a lot of "built-up" energy when in distress? This is a common physiological response called the "fight or flight" response. It's an automatic reaction triggered by the brain's perception of a threat or stressor. When faced with a challenging or threatening situation, the body prepares to either confront the threat (fight) or escape it (flight).

When OCD is triggered, the resulting anxiety and distress trigger this "fight or flight" response. So, the goal of Intense Exercise here is to help you expend all that built-up energy.

What's your go-to intense physical activity?

Examples: running, HIIT sessions, indoor/outdoor cycling, etc.

(1) ____________________

(2) ____________________

(3) ____________________

(4) ____________________

(5) ____________________

P

Paced Breathing.

Slow, deep breathing can activate the parasympathetic nervous system, or PNS, which helps calm the body's stress response. By practicing paced breathing, you can reduce anxiety and regain a sense of control over your emotions, making it easier to resist engaging in compulsive behaviors driven by OCD.

Tip: Do any or all of the Mindfulness breathing exercises in this book.

P

Paired Muscle Relaxation.

Pairing muscle relaxation techniques with paced breathing can help release physical tension in the body, which is often associated with stress and anxiety. This can lead to a reduction in emotional distress and compulsive urges.

What to do: Tighten your muscles steadily while taking a deep breath, but not so much that they cramp. Exhale slowly, allowing your stiff muscles to relax.

Emotion Regulation

If you remember, Emotion Regulation is one of the key components distinguishing DBT from OCD. This skill is about how we react to things outside ourselves, helping us understand and respond to our surroundings.

With OCD, when unwanted thoughts or images invade our minds, we interpret them exaggeratedly or catastrophically (e.g., something bad will happen). This interpretation then creates a lot of strong and unpleasant emotions in us, such as anxiety, fear, distress, and so on. As a result, we feel almost duty-bound to behave in such a way that eases the burden of our unpleasant feelings.

So, **Unwanted Thoughts -> Unpleasant Emotions -> Induced Behavior**. But what if you can "hijack" the emotion part? Suppose you can learn ways to regulate and control unpleasant emotions. In that case, there's a big chance you can avoid doing the induced behavior, right?

Before we proceed, I'd like to emphasize that **your emotions are valid**. You are not imagining it, nor are you deliberately exaggerating it. The intense emotions you feel are due to your OCD.

So, please know that Emotion Regulation skills are NOT about ignoring or invalidating your feelings. It's about learning how to control your emotions better so they don't control you.

Emotion Regulation skills differ from Distress Tolerance skills in that they focus on taking action to lessen the intensity of an emotional experience. In contrast, Distress Tolerance skills focus on surviving the moment.

Worksheet: Build Positive Experiences (BPE)

Increase positivity to reduce negativity. Research shows that happy people are less vulnerable to unpleasant emotions[22], so this exercise teaches you how to accumulate more positive, happy moments in your life.

Build Positive Experiences I

List down 10 activities that make you happy. These "feel good" things should make you happy while doing them or soon after.

Examples: walking in nature, doing yoga, volunteering, etc.

1.

2.

3.

4.

5.

6.

7.

8.

9.

10.

Build Positive Experiences II

Choose ONE thing from the list above that you will do every day. No matter what you plan to do or how long you want to do it, it doesn't matter. The goal is to do the activity EACH AND EVERY DAY. (Make being happy a daily routine!)

Example: practicing yoga

I will <u>practice yoga</u> every morning for <u>30 minutes</u>.

Your turn:

I choose: ____

I will ____________________ every day for ____________________.

Build Positive Experiences III

List down 10 activities that have the potential to provide you with long-term enjoyment. You may have to plan these activities, but engaging in them should make your life better in the long run.

Examples: getting a pet, gardening, learning how to cook, etc.

1.

2.

3.

4.

5.

6.

7.

8.

9.

10.

Worksheet: Emotional Awareness Journaling for OCD

This exercise will help you increase your emotional awareness and comprehension of OCD-related thoughts, emotions, and actions. Here's how to do this:

1. Set Your Intention

Begin by setting your intention for your journaling practice. Remind yourself that the purpose is to cultivate emotional awareness and gain insights into your OCD-related experiences.

What's your intention statement?

Example: I want to understand OCD and its effects on me more—without judgment.

____

____

____

2. Identify Your Trigger

Write down the specific trigger or situation that prompted the emotional response related to your OCD. This can be a specific thought, situation, or event that triggered anxiety or distress. (**Tip**: If you want to dive deeper, try the ***Know Your OCD Triggers*** exercise on page 166.)

What triggers your OCD?

Example: whenever anyone asks me to clean my room

____

____

____

3. Describe Your Emotions

Identify and describe the primary emotion you experienced in response to the trigger. Use descriptive words to capture the intensity and quality of the emotion.

What emotions are you experiencing?

Example: I feel really anxious. I don't want to part with any of my stuff.

4. Notice Physical Manifestations of Your Emotions

Pay attention to any physical sensations associated with your feelings. Close your eyes, take a few deep breaths, and scan your body. Notice any tension, discomfort, or other physical sensations accompanying the emotion. After identifying where you're feeling your emotions, focus on relieving them.

WHERE are you feeling your emotions?

Example: I feel heaviness on my chest. My breathing is rapidly increasing.

WHAT do you want to do about how your feelings appear in your body?

Example: I'm going to Square Breathe (page 41) until the heavy feeling in my chest disappears.

5. Observe Your Thoughts and Beliefs

Become aware of the thoughts and beliefs that arise when experiencing the emotion related to your OCD. Write down the specific thoughts that contribute to the emotional response. Recognize any thought patterns that are irrational, biased, or exaggerated.

What are your thoughts and beliefs?

Example: I don't want to throw or give anything away because I will need them later. Also, if my stuff doesn't stay exactly how it is now, I'll never find anything. And if I can't find something I need, something bad will happen.

____

____

____

6. Challenge Your Irrational, Biased, or Exaggerated Thoughts

Take a closer look at the thoughts identified in the previous step. Challenge any irrational beliefs by examining the evidence for and against them. Try to replace them with more balanced and realistic perspectives.

Exaggerated Thought	Realistic Thought
Example: I don't want to throw or give anything away because I will need them later.	*Example: I DON'T know if I'll need any of these things later. And even if I do, I can easily get another one.*

7. Validate and Reflect

Acknowledge and validate your emotional experience. Offer yourself compassion and understanding for the challenges you face with OCD. Reflect that emotions are natural responses, and it is okay to feel what you feel.

8. Practice Self-Compassion

Write a self-compassionate statement or affirmation to support yourself during this emotional experience. Offer kind and comforting words to yourself, acknowledging that you are doing your best to manage your OCD.

What's your self-compassion statement?

Example: I'm having unpleasant thoughts and emotions right now, and that's fine. OCD is difficult, but my thoughts and feelings don't define me. OCD is something I have, not who I am. I'm resilient and strong and will be kind to myself as I go through this. Like everyone, I'm worthy of love and sympathy. I will take the necessary precautions to care for myself during this difficult time.

____

____

____

____

____

____

9. Takeaways and Insights

Reflect on any insights or new understandings you gained from this journaling exercise. Consider what you can learn from your emotions and how they relate to your OCD. Note any patterns, triggers, or coping strategies that emerge.

Remember, this journaling exercise is a personal exploration, so feel free to adapt and modify it to best suit your needs.

Worksheet: PLEASE

Your physical health directly affects your emotional and mental health.[23,24] When your body is well-nourished and rested, you are better equipped to manage stress and anxiety associated with OCD. This exercise will help you prioritize taking care of your body.

PL

Treat Physical illness.

Fighting unwanted thoughts and unpleasant emotions is harder when you're physically sick. So, if you're ill, don't put off seeing a doctor or taking any prescribed medications. It's also a good idea to arrange for someone (e.g., a family member, friend, neighbor, etc.) to accompany you so you're not alone while you're sick.

If you don't want to or cannot see a doctor, consider a holistic approach to treatment, such as acupuncture, aromatherapy, acupressure, yoga, etc. The goal is to recover as quickly as possible.

When was the last time you were physically ill?

____

Did you see a doctor? Y / N

Why or why not?

____

____

____

E	**Balance Your Eating.** A balanced diet gives you the nutrients and energy you need to live a healthy life, which includes controlling your feelings and dealing with stress. Your food affects your overall health, so nourishing your body with food that affects you positively is important. One tip is to try and eat food as close to its natural state as much as possible. For example, pan grill some chicken breasts instead of eating high-calorie, high-sodium, ultra-processed chicken nuggets from the supermarket. Also, instead of consuming drinks high in sugar and artificial ingredients, switch to healthier alternatives like plain water or herbal tea.
A	**Avoid Unhealthy Substances.** Refrain from using alcohol or drugs to cope with stress or emotions. Substance use can intensify emotional responses and interfere with effective coping.
S	**Sleep Regularly.** Quality sleep is essential for emotional regulation and overall well-being. But how much sleep should you get? According to the American Academy of Sleep Medicine (AAS), adults need at least seven (7) hours of quality sleep every night.[25] Quality sleep is defined as restful and undisturbed sleep that allows you to wake up refreshed and rejuvenated. Establishing a consistent sleeping routine is beneficial to ensure you get optimal sleep. This means aiming to go to bed and wake up at the same

	time every night. By following a regular schedule, your body can develop a natural sleep-wake cycle, leading to better sleep quality and improved well-being.
E	**Exercise.** Engage in regular physical activities that you enjoy. Exercise releases *endorphins*, which can improve mood and reduce stress. The World Health Organization recommends that adults aged 18-64 aim for at least 2.5 to 5 hours of moderate-intensity aerobic physical activity or 1.25 to 2.5 hours of vigorous aerobic physical activity weekly. Additionally, it is beneficial to include muscle-strengthening activities of moderate to high intensity at least 2 times per week. Following these guidelines can significantly contribute to improving overall health and well-being.

Important: PLEASE skills are not intended as one-time activities. Incorporating these practices into your daily life is key to experiencing their full benefits. Strive to make them an integral part of your lifestyle, as consistent application will enhance their effectiveness and positive impact.

Worksheet: Check the Facts

This exercise is a simple and effective way to handle unwanted and irrational thoughts and images. When you experience a thought that makes you feel anxious or distressed, take a moment to examine whether the thought is based on reality or if it's a product of OCD. By doing this, you can gain better control over your thoughts and reduce their impact on your emotions. In short, when you take a moment to question and apply logic to strong emotions, these strong emotions will start to subside. You will feel better. And when you start to feel better, it's less likely that you will behave (act) in unpleasant or unproductive ways.

Let's start with a reflective exercise. Think back to a previous situation when you may have given into urges (compulsions) too quickly in response to your emotions.

Question: What's the thought that triggered your OCD? *Example: I'm afraid I will harm someone unintentionally.*
Question: What emotion related to this OCD thought do you want to fact-check? *Example: my feelings of anxiety and distress*
Your answer:

Question: Looking back, on a scale of 1-5, how would you rate your distress? (1 = manageable stress, 5 = unmanageable distress):

Example: A strong 4.

Your answer:

Question: What assumptions did you make due to this OCD thought?

Example: Because I thought of harming someone, I assumed I would harm someone soon.

Your answer:

Question: What did you do to relieve your strong emotions?

Example: I did what I always do; I took a handful of rice and started counting the grains.

Your answer:

Now, it's time to CHECK THE FACTS!

You listed your assumptions above, but <u>WHAT ELSE</u> could be true?

To help you, try to answer these questions:

- *What evidence is there to support this thought?*

  Example: I don't have any.

- *What evidence is there to <u>contradict</u> this thought?*

  Examples:

  I have NEVER harmed anyone in my life. I don't even raise my voice even when I'm upset.

  I have NEVER harmed any of my pets.

- *Have I ever acted on this thought in the past?*

  Example: No.

- *How likely is it that this thought will come true?*

  Example: Not likely.

Your answers:

Question: After answering the above questions, are your OCD thoughts supported by FACTS?

Example: No.

Your answer:

Question: Why do you think you reacted that way? *Example: I didn't take the time to evaluate my thoughts. I just reacted to them.*
Your answer:
Question: Looking back, on a scale of 0-5, did your emotion fit the facts? (0 = not at all, 5 = yes): *Example: 0*
Your answer:
Question: What would you do differently if your emotion did not fit the facts? *Example: First, I would practice Mindfulness (page 38) and then do Distress Tolerance exercises (page 45) to ease my anxiety and distress. Then I'd do* ***Check the Facts*** *to put my thoughts and emotions into perspective.*
Your answer:

Note: The **Check the Facts** exercise can be used whenever you experience unpleasant emotions. It's not just a one-time reflection but a tool you can use repeatedly. To make it more effective, I suggest practicing this exercise at least two more times to develop the habit of fact-checking your emotions regularly. Doing so can strengthen your emotional resilience and gain better control over your responses to unwanted thoughts or OCD-triggering situations.

Interpersonal Effectiveness

Interpersonal Effectiveness is the art of learning how to effectively communicate your wants and needs to others. OCD is largely an internal struggle, so why need Interpersonal Effectiveness skills? Because we all need meaningful relationships in our lives.

Our connections and relationships with other people affect our general happiness and well-being. Healthy and helpful relationships give us mental support, a sense of belonging, and the chance to share our joys and struggles. Strong social connections can also help us get through hard times by making us feel safe and understood.

Great relationships are important in OCD treatment. But to build these relationships, you must learn to better explain your internal experiences and struggles and address problems with others.

Furthermore, better interpersonal skills reduce the likelihood of misunderstandings and conflict with others, which can prompt strong emotions that can trigger your OCD.

Content Warning: the following story contains distressing material.

This is what Michael†, a reader, had to say: "*I found the girl of my dreams in Rose and ruined our relationship with my OCD. I have Contamination OCD, and the pandemic heightened my anxiety over germs. I know some OCD sufferers felt relief during COVID because people always used hand sanitizers and gels. Still, it had the opposite effect on me. I became more paranoid. At one point, my hands were red and raw from my constant*

† *Name changed for privacy.*

washing, scrubbing, sanitizing... and then doing this ritual all over again.

At first, Rose was understanding because I told her about my OCD before we moved in together (a year before COVID). However, my OCD-ness started to extend to her. I couldn't get near her because I irrationally thought she wasn't washing and sanitizing enough. This led to the compulsion to grab the hand sanitizer and try to spray her with it, which angered her, of course.

We tried to talk about it, but my brain went back to trying to spray her. Even when she washes and sprays in front of me, my mind plays tricks, and I still doubt her as if she's lying to me. Pretty soon, talking about the situation just brought out anger in me. I couldn't properly verbalize what was happening, and honestly, I didn't know what I needed from her.

Rose left the minute lockdown measures eased a bit. I was left alone and felt utter relief. I was happy she was gone! But that lasted only a few days. Depression started to set in, and I started to obsess about the stove and harming myself. In complete desperation, I called my mother. She connected me to a distant uncle who was a psychiatrist. Very slowly, I got better, but Rose was already long gone. If only I had the tools to address my OCD with Rose, maybe things would have ended differently.

On the next page is a "classic" DBT exercise. It's a great technique to start effectively discussing OCD with other people.

Worksheet: DEARMAN

DEARMAN is a DBT exercise focusing on effectively communicating with others and getting support. DEARMAN is made up of two components:

- **DEAR**: **What to do** to get what you want.
- **MAN**: **How to ask** effectively.

Describe the situation and your feelings related to your OCD. When speaking, describe your circumstances clearly, and do your best not to relay any opinions or judgments. Stick to the facts.

Example: I wanted to talk to you about something important. I have been living with OCD, a mental health condition that causes me to have recurring thoughts and perform certain rituals or behaviors. I feel anxious, overwhelmed, and sometimes even frustrated because of it.

____

____

____

____

____

Express your thoughts and feelings about your OCD and its impact on your life. Don't assume the other person knows what you're going through, so use '**I**' statements.

Example: I feel trapped living with my OCD. It often feels like I'm in a constant loop of intrusive thoughts and compulsions. It affects my daily life, making simple tasks take longer and causing great distress. I really want you to understand how much I struggle, and your support is important to me.

____

____

____

____

____

Assert yourself. Clearly state what you need from your family and friends. Be specific about what you're requesting.

Example: It would mean a lot to me if you could try to learn more about OCD, its symptoms, and how it affects people's lives. By understanding my challenges, maybe you can offer me a compassionate ear when I need to talk about my experiences or provide gentle reminders when my OCD becomes overwhelming.

____

____

____

____

____

Reinforce your request. Tell the other person you will be grateful if they give in to your request. However, DO NOT insist, coerce or use emotional blackmailing tactics.

Example: Having your support will truly make a difference in how I manage my OCD, and I will feel less alone in this struggle of mine.

____

____

____

____

____

Mindfulness. Maintain a calm and composed demeanor during the conversation and stay focused on your main points. The calmer you are, the more the other person will realize the importance of the topic to you.

Example: I want to emphasize that I'm sharing this with you because I trust and value your presence and support. I understand that discussing mental health can be uncomfortable or unfamiliar. However, I must know I'm in an environment where I feel safe and supported.

Appear confident. Show confidence in your words and body language to convey the importance of your request.

Example: I'm being honest about my OCD because your acceptance and support are important. That's why I'm asking you to educate yourself about OCD. I know it will make a difference in my life and our relationship.

Negotiate. If the individual you're speaking with disagrees with your request, be willing to compromise. You can suggest an alternative solution or ask them what they believe should happen next.

Example: Do you have any questions about OCD or concerns you want to address? Let's work together to find ways that you can support me in managing my OCD, whether it's by learning about my triggers or helping me implement healthy coping mechanisms.

Worksheet: Communicating Boundaries

This exercise is designed to assist individuals with OCD in effectively communicating their boundaries to others, particularly regarding their OCD-related needs and triggers. Here's how to do this:

1. Self-Reflection

Reflect on how your OCD affects your interactions with others and daily life. Identify specific OCD-related triggers, stressors, and the type of support you may need from those around you.

Example: When I get stressed at work, especially when deadlines are looming, this is when my OCD is triggered. I need the support of my immediate boss.

____

____

____

____

____

2. Identify Key OCD-Related Boundaries

List the boundaries that are important for managing your OCD.

Examples:

- *No jokes or side comments about my OCD.*
- *No last-minute piling of tasks.*
- *No to colleagues leaving stuff on my desk. (The clutter triggers me.)*

____

____

____

____

____

3. Prepare Clear Statements

Craft clear statements that express your OCD-related boundaries in an assertive but non-confrontational manner.

Examples:

- *I'm asking you to please refrain from making jokes or side comments about my OCD.*
- *I get stressed out when I get last-minute tasks with short deadlines. It triggers my OCD.*
- *I need to keep my space clean and organized as it helps me manage my OCD. So please don't just leave stuff on my desk.*

____

____

____

____

____

4. Practice with Someone You Trust

Role-play with a trusted friend or family member to practice communicating your OCD-related boundaries. Experiment with different scenarios to build your confidence.

5. Utilize "I" Statements

Use "I" statements when communicating your boundaries. Remember, these are *your* feelings and needs related to OCD. And even though these are important, you're still making a request from others. (See item #3 above for examples of "I" statements.)

6. Be Clear and Specific

In addition to being clear about your boundaries, clearly express the supportive and helpful behaviors for you. You should also mention what you consider to be triggering or unhelpful. Be specific about the kind of support you need during difficult times.

Example: I feel overwhelmed when you try to accommodate my OCD. I should handle it myself, but your support is still appreciated.

7. **Emphasize Positive Intent**

Reassure others that setting boundaries is about caring for yourself and fostering healthier relationships.

Example: Thank you for hearing me out. I just want to mention that these boundaries not only help me deal with my OCD; they also make me a more productive employee and better co-worker.

8. **Use Active Listening**

Encourage the other person to share their thoughts and feelings about your OCD-related boundaries. Practice active listening to understand their perspective while maintaining your needs.

Example: Do you have any questions about OCD or concerns about my boundaries?

9. Be Patient and Flexible

Be patient with others as they adjust to your boundaries. Not everyone may fully understand or accept them right away. Stay open to discussion and adjustments if needed.

10. Reevaluate and Adjust

Regularly reevaluate your OCD-related boundaries to ensure they align with your evolving needs.

Worksheet: GIVE

The previous worksheets emphasized the importance of effective communication in expressing *your* needs to others. Now, let's delve into **GIVE**, which revolves around considering the other person(s) involved in the conversation.

The core objective of **GIVE** is to nurture positive interactions. Simply put, you aim for the other person to feel positive and valued during the conversation. When they have a positive experience, they are more likely to be receptive to your request.

G	**Be Gentle.** Remind yourself to approach situations with kindness and compassion towards yourself and the other person. For example, say you're at work, and a coworker accidentally touches your desk, triggering obsessive thoughts about contamination. You may feel anxious or angry. However, communicating these emotions to your coworker doesn't help anyone. It may even escalate the situation. Instead, take a deep breath and gently and mindfully say, "I get anxious when you touch my desk, Jack. It triggers my OCD. So can you please be mindful of that?" **List five ways to ask for something in a nice way.** *Example: talk with mindfulness and kindness, look directly at the other person but don't stare them down, etc.*

	1. ____ 2. ____ 3. ____ 4. ____ 5. ____
I	**Act Interested.** Show genuine interest in the other person's perspective, even if it challenges your OCD-related beliefs. **List five ways you convey interest.** *Examples: maintain eye contact during the conversation, don't interrupt, don't do other things while they're talking, etc.* 1. ____ 2. ____ 3. ____ 4. ____ 5. ____
V	**Validate.** Acknowledge the other person's feelings and experiences, even if they don't align with your OCD-driven fears. **List five ways you validate others.** *Examples: repeat what the other person said, nod your head as they're trying to make a point to show you understand their perspective, look interested (not bored), etc.*

	1. __________ 2. __________ 3. __________ 4. __________ 5. __________
E	**Show an Easy Manner.** Maintain a friendly and non-confrontational demeanor to foster a positive atmosphere. **List 5 ways you can show friendliness.** *Examples: smile, use open body language, avoid signs of hostility or discomfort, etc.* 1. __________ 2. __________ 3. __________ 4. __________ 5. __________

While this chapter on DBT for OCD may be concise, the skills it offers are incredibly valuable. As you proceed to the next chapter, which delves into CBT as an effective treatment for OCD, you'll discover how these skills can significantly impact your well-being and aid in your journey toward managing OCD symptoms effectively.

Overcoming OCD Using CBT Techniques

"CBT helps individuals with OCD develop a new relationship with their intrusive thoughts, allowing them to resist engaging in rituals and regain control over their lives."
– Steven J. Seay

Cognitive refers to **how you think**. It's anything related to the process of cognition, which involves mental activities associated with thinking, understanding, perceiving, remembering, reasoning, and problem-solving.

Behavioral refers to **how you behave**, i.e., your actions, responses, and observable activities.

Therapy refers to a process of **treatment or intervention** aimed at improving a person's mental, emotional, or physical well-being.

So, CBT aims to improve a person's well-being by transforming negative thought patterns (obsessions) and maladaptive behaviors (compulsions).

If you recall the OCD cycle (page 21), it can be assumed that everything initiates with the onset of obsessions (unwanted, irrational thoughts). Although OCD is a complicated condition with numerous causes and risk factors, the cornerstone of CBT treatment is the belief that obsessions are characterized by *cognitive distortions*, also called "thinking errors" or "thinking biases."[26,27,28]

Cognitive Distortions: Understanding Mind Traps

Individuals with OCD, according to the cognitive model, have *faulty* thoughts and beliefs that contribute to the development and maintenance of their obsessions and compulsions. Among these cognitive distortions are:

1. **Catastrophic Thinking** (a.k.a. *Catastrophizing*) is believing that if a specific feared event were to occur, it would be catastrophic or unbearable. The "worst-case scenario" is the default way of thinking here. Example: You receive an email from your boss requesting to discuss something with you in their office tomorrow morning. You start worrying that you must have done something terribly wrong and will get fired. Your thoughts spiral further, imagining losing your job, being unable to find another place of employment, and finally, complete financial ruin.

2. **Overestimation of Threats** is overestimating the likelihood or severity of negative outcomes related to obsessions. Example: Fearing that touching a doorknob will lead to a life-threatening illness from which there is no possibility of being cured.

3. **Thought-Action Fusion** (a.k.a. *Over-Importance of Thoughts* or *Magical Thinking*) is believing that having a distressing thought is morally equivalent to performing the feared action. In short, you equate the mere presence of the thought with being responsible for its potential consequences in the real world. Example: You have a sudden, unwanted thought about harming a family member. You believe this thought alone automatically makes you a terrible person, and you might actually harm your family member.

4. **All-or-Nothing Thinking** (a.k.a. *Black-and-White Thinking*) sees situations only in black-and-white terms, ignoring life's many gray areas or complexities. In other words, it's either a total success or a complete failure,

with no room for anything in between. Example: If you can't do a report perfectly, you're a complete failure at work.

5. **Inflated Sense of Responsibility** is feeling an exaggerated responsibility for preventing harm or negative outcomes, even when there is no realistic connection between your actions and the feared consequences. Example: You fear the house will burn down if you don't knock on the door three times.

6. **Emotionalizing** is when you let your emotions heavily influence your thoughts and interpretations of events without considering objective evidence or alternative perspectives. It involves viewing situations or experiences solely through an emotional lens, leading to skewed perceptions and irrational reactions. Example: You had a simple disagreement with a friend, and you think it's a sign that the friendship is over.

Now that you're familiar with the most common cognitive distortions in OCD, let's delve into the process of challenging, restructuring, or reframing these "thinking errors" using CBT.

Tip: Before attempting any of the exercises in the next chapters, it would be highly beneficial if you re-familiarize yourself with the DBT concepts of Acceptance + Change, Mindfulness, Distress Tolerance, and Emotion Regulation.

Cognitive Restructuring for OCD

Cognitive restructuring focuses on discovering irrational, negative, or distorted thought patterns and modifying them to be more effective. The phrase "more effective" here means seeing things clearer, and applying reason or logic to your thoughts to elicit less negative emotions, thus allowing for more skillful behavior.

The following are various cognitive restructuring techniques. These techniques aim to make you feel better, so I encourage you to try them with an open mind and see which one is most beneficial to you.

Thought Monitoring

It all begins with our thoughts. Thought monitoring is a technique that involves becoming aware of and tracking one's thoughts, particularly automatic or intrusive thoughts that arise in various situations. In the context of OCD, thought monitoring plays a crucial role in helping individuals recognize and challenge their obsessive thoughts.

Worksheet: Thought Monitoring

1. Identify Obsessive Thought Patterns

Reflect on the most common obsessive thought patterns related to your OCD. These thoughts are intrusive, unwanted, and cause distress. Write down each obsessive thought as it arises throughout the day. Be specific and record the exact thought as it occurs.

Examples:
What if I forgot to turn off the stove? The house might burn down.
I must have contaminated my hands with germs somewhere. I must wash them again.
Oh my God, how will I get out of this room? I need to reach the door by walking in a straight line, but someone is standing in my way.

____

____

____

____

____

2. Rate Your Anxiety

Next to each obsessive thought, rate your anxiety level on a scale from 0 to 10, with 0 being no anxiety and 10 being extreme anxiety. This helps you track the intensity of the distress caused by each thought.

Example: What if I forgot to turn off the stove? The house might burn down.
Anxiety Level: 8/10

3. Challenge Cognitive Distortions

Identify cognitive distortions present in each of your obsessive thoughts. Common cognitive distortions include catastrophizing, black-and-white thinking, and emotional reasoning. (See also Cognitive Distortion: Understanding Mind Traps, page 82.) Challenge these distortions by asking yourself questions such as:

What evidence do I have to support this thought?
Are my thoughts based on facts or assumptions?
That worst-case scenario in my head, how likely is it to happen?

(**Tip**: You may want to review DBT's Check the Facts exercise on page 65.)

4. Generate Alternative Thoughts

Think of more balanced and realistic alternative thoughts for each obsessive thought you have. Consider the fact or evidence against the catastrophic outcomes and adopt a more rational perspective.

Example:
Obsessive Thought: What if I forgot to turn off the stove? The house might burn down.
Alternative Thought: I remember checking the stove, and it's unlikely I left it on. I'll trust my memory and move on.

5. Rate Your Anxiety Levels Again

After generating alternative thoughts, re-rate your anxiety levels for each obsessive thought. Notice how challenging cognitive distortions and adopting a rational perspective impact your anxiety level.

Example:
Obsessive Thought: What if I forgot to turn off the stove? The house might burn down.
Anxiety Level: 8/10
Alternative Thought: I remember checking the stove, and it's unlikely I left it on. I can trust my memory and move on.
New Anxiety Level: 5/10

6. Practice, Practice, Practice!

Practice thought monitoring daily and review your notes regularly to identify patterns in your obsessive thoughts and the effectiveness of challenging cognitive distortions. Over time, you'll develop greater awareness of your thought patterns and build resilience against OCD-related anxieties.

Here's a sample **Thought Monitoring Log** incorporating the above steps.

Thought Monitoring Log				
Obsessive Thought	**Anxiety Level**	**Challenge Cognitive Distortion**	**Alternative Thoughts**	**New Anxiety Level**
I must have contaminated my hands with germs somewhere. I need to wash them again.	*7/10*	*What evidence do I have to support this thought?* *I don't have any facts to support this thought. I must be catastrophizing.*	*I just washed my hands AND used a hand sanitizer gel. I know I'm clean. I can move on now.*	*4/10*

Re-Thinking Thoughts: Challenging Mind Traps

If you find it difficult to challenge your cognitive distortions during the Thought Monitoring exercise above, that's completely normal and okay. It takes time to become accustomed to thinking differently, so be kind and patient with yourself.

If Thought Monitoring covers various thoughts, the following exercise is designed to target and challenge specific obsessive thoughts related to your OCD. The best way to carry out this exercise, especially if it's your first time to do so, is to focus on ONE specific thinking bias and ONE specific situation. By narrowing your focus, you can thoroughly "unpack" the situation and better understand the cognitive distortion at play.

Further, this targeted approach allows you to delve into the details and explore how the bias impacts your thoughts and emotions in that specific scenario. As you become more comfortable with the process, you can expand to other biases and situations, gradually building your ability to challenge and reframe different obsessive thoughts related to your OCD. Remember, starting small and focused can lead to significant insights and progress along your journey to better mental well-being.

Worksheet: Challenging Your Specific Thinking Biases

1. Identify Your Specific Thinking Bias

What specific OCD thinking bias (cognitive distortion) do you suffer from? (See Cognitive Distortions: Understanding Mind Traps on page 82 for a description of these thinking biases.)

- ☐ Catastrophic Thinking
- ☐ Overestimation of Threat
- ☐ Thought-Action Fusion (a.k.a. Over-Importance of Thoughts or Magical Thinking)
- ☐ All-or-Nothing Thinking (a.k.a. Black-and-White Thinking)
- ☐ Inflated Sense of Responsibility
- ☐ Emotionalizing

2. Provide Details Surrounding the Thinking Bias (What Happened?)

You may have more than one thinking bias, but for now, select one. Next, write down what happened to trigger this obsessive thought. Be as detailed as you can.

What is your specific thinking bias?

Thinking Bias: *Emotionalizing*

What happened?

What Happened: *My best friend and I had a miscommunication. I thought we scheduled lunch for tomorrow. She thought it was for today, so she waited an hour for lunch for me. When I checked our messages, I realized I was wrong; it WAS for today. I apologized, and she said it was fine, but I think she was annoyed. I just texted her again, but she's not answering. I'm afraid it's a sign that our friendship is over.*

3. Evaluate and Challenge Irrational Beliefs

In the abovementioned situation, please answer the following questions as best you can.

- What's the specific thought you're obsessing about in this situation?

  Example: My friendship with my best friend is over.

- Are your thoughts based on Facts or Feelings? Choose one.

  ☐ Facts

  ☐ Feelings

- Would you classify your thoughts as Knowing or Guessing? Choose one.

  ☐ Knowing

  ☐ Guessing

- List down any evidence that supports your thoughts.

  Example: We had a big argument years ago, and she ghosted me for a while.

- What are alternative explanations or interpretations for this situation? WHAT ELSE can be true?

  Examples:

  My friend is in a meeting so she can't answer my message.

  My friend is talking to someone on her phone, so she might've not seen my message yet.

  My friend could be somewhere without an internet connection, so she might've not seen my message yet.

  ____

  ____

  ____

  ____

  ____

4. **Reflect on the Past**

   Have you experienced thoughts like this in the past? If you have, did your assumptions turn out to be true? It's essential to reflect on your previous experiences to gain insight into the accuracy of your thoughts and whether they align with reality.

   Examples:

   My sister, with whom I'm very close, moved to a different state a year ago. I was devastated and couldn't help but feel she wanted to escape from me, tired of me and my OCD. She said she moved because of a great work opportunity, but I didn't believe her. Fortunately, she didn't let go. She consistently tried to stay in touch and keep our connection strong. When I finally had the chance to visit her and see her new life, it became clear that she truly was pursuing what was best for her, and my fears were unfounded.

   A few months ago, a co-worker banged his chair against his desk and left for home. I thought I did something to make him really mad. It turned out he was just in a hurry to leave because he was late for his son's birthday. It didn't have anything to do with me.

5. The Verdict

Reflecting on your answers above, are your thoughts based on logic, evidence, or facts, or is it an OCD exaggeration? Choose one.

- ☐ Logic, evidence, facts
- ☐ OCD exaggeration

Whenever you notice intrusive obsessive thoughts, consciously challenge them using the above exercise. Challenge these irrational thoughts repeatedly and consistently to strengthen new thought patterns over time.

Where's the link?

In addition to the above exercise, something that I personally found helpful in challenging my cognitive distortions is asking myself this question: *Where's the link?*

For example, sometimes I would experience the compulsion to perform a specific action (e.g., arranging my toiletries in alphabetical order) to maintain high sales in my business. So, I ask myself, "Where's the link?" How is arranging my toiletries in alphabetical order linked to sales? After asking this question, my mind starts to recognize that there's no direct correlation between my compulsion and my business. I then say, "Ah, this is my OCD." This simple process of challenging my thoughts and acknowledging my OCD helps me break free from the cycle and reduce the impact of my intrusive thoughts.

Socratic Questioning

Socratic Questioning is a powerful and important strategy in CBT. It entails a specific form of questioning to help you examine and challenge your thoughts, beliefs, and assumptions. This method is named after the Greek philosopher *Socrates*, who employed the same question-and-answer (Q&A) style to encourage critical thinking and self-discovery.

Worksheet: Socratic Questioning

In the exercise below, we use contamination and cleaning OCD as an example to show how Socratic Questioning works. However, you can easily change it to address your OCD symptoms. The key is to use the same self-inquiry and critical thinking process to question and restructure your obsessive thoughts and compulsive behaviors.

Q1: What specific obsession causes you great distress?

Example: I fear germs on my hands after touching everyday objects.

____

____

____

Q2: How does this obsession impact your daily life and overall well-being?

Example: It makes me anxious and leads to excessive cleaning, which takes up A LOT of my time.

____

____

____

Q3: What evidence do you have that supports your belief?

Example: I've gotten sick in the past after touching dirty surfaces.

____

____

____

Q4: Can you think of any evidence that <u>contradicts</u> your belief? Have there been times when you touched objects without getting sick?

Example: Well, yes, there have been many times I touched things without getting sick.

___

___

___

Q5: Let's evaluate the likelihood of your feared outcome, such as getting seriously ill from touching everyday objects. How often does that happen to most people?

Example: It's rare for someone to get seriously ill from touching everyday stuff.

___

___

___

Q6: What are some alternative explanations for your experiences? Could there be other reasons for you getting sick on those occasions? WHAT ELSE could have caused your illness?

Example: I could've gotten sick from other sources, like coming into contact with a sick person.

___

___

___

Q7: If you don't engage in cleaning compulsions, what's the worst-case scenario you fear will happen?

Example: I worry I might contract a serious illness without a cure. I also worry I might pass it on to my loved ones.

___

___

___

Q8: Let's explore the likelihood of this worst-case scenario occurring. How likely is it, considering you have taken reasonable precautions like handwashing?

Example: It's not very likely, especially if I follow basic hygiene practices.

Q9: Do you think there are any cognitive distortions present in your thinking, such as catastrophizing or all-or-nothing thinking?

Example: Well, I guess I tend to catastrophize the consequences of not cleaning obsessively.

Q10: Can you recall when you resisted the compulsion to immediately wash your hands after touching daily objects? How did you feel during and after that experience?

Example: I remember feeling anxious and extremely uncomfortable during the moment, but nothing bad happened afterwards.

Q11: Based on the evidence and your experiences, is your initial belief still valid?

Example: No, it seems less valid now that I've examined the evidence and challenged my thinking.

Q12: How would you approach future situations that trigger your contamination fears? What strategies can you implement to manage your anxiety without excessive cleaning?

Example: I could practice using hand sanitizer or remind myself that germs won't necessarily harm me immediately.

____

____

____

Q13: What can you do to reinforce and practice this new approach of challenging your contamination fears and reducing compulsions?

Example: I'll start by resisting the compulsion to wash my hands immediately and see how it goes. I can keep track of my progress in a journal.

____

____

____

Q14: How can you ensure you implement the changes you mentioned above? How can you monitor your progress?

Example: I'll use my journal to record when I started challenging my irrational thoughts. I'll also ask the help of my older brother, whom I trust completely, to help me be accountable.

____

____

____

Coping Self-Talk

Coping Self-Talk (a.k.a. Positive Self-Talk) is a cognitive coping strategy that involves consciously changing one's thoughts and *inner dialogue* to be more positive, encouraging, and constructive. This technique aims to replace negative or unhelpful thoughts with more rational, supportive, and optimistic ones.

Here's a quick example of how this technique works:

Negative Thought: I know the Project Report I submitted at work contains some errors. Why did I even submit it? I'm such a loser! Why would anybody at work trust me now? I'll probably lose my job over this.

Coping Self-Talk: It's okay to make mistakes; it's part of learning, and I'm human, after all. I can take it one step at a time and improve with practice.

Worksheet: Coping Self-Talk

1. **Identify Obsessive Thought**

   Start by recognizing the specific obsessive thought that triggers your OCD.

   Example: If I didn't turn the kitchen faucet off properly, the house might get flooded!

   ____

   ____

   ____

2. **Observe Emotions**

   Notice the emotions that arise with your obsessive thought.

   Example: I'm feeling really frantic and anxious right now.

   ____

   ____

   ____

3. **Practice Mindfulness**

   Take a moment to pause and take a few deep breaths. This will help create space between the obsessive thought and your reaction to it. (Try Belly Breathing or Square Breathing, pages 40 and 41, respectively.)

4. **Tolerate Initial Distress**

   Remember, you're not as fragile as you think. Urge Surf (page 47) or practice STOP (page 49) to survive the initial onslaught of anxiety brought on by obsessive thoughts.

5. **Challenge the Thought**

   Question the validity of your obsessive thought.

   Example: My OCD is making me think this. Before I left, I checked the tap.

6. **Reframe with Coping Self-Talk**

   Develop a positive and rational coping statement to counter the anxiety and distress caused by obsessive thoughts.

   Examples:

   I checked the faucet before I left; nothing bad will happen.

   It's normal to have doubts, but I can trust my previous checks and not give in to the compulsion.

7. **Practice Self-Compassion**

   Be kind to yourself and acknowledge that everyone experiences intrusive thoughts. Replace self-criticism with self-compassionate statements.

   Example: Having these thoughts is okay; they don't define who I am.

8. **Accept Uncertainty**

   Embrace the reality that uncertainty is a natural part of life. Let go of the need to control everything and recognize that not all uncertainties must be addressed.

   Examples:

   I can handle uncertainty, and not all thoughts are facts.

   I'm stronger than I think I am. Even if something negative happens, I can handle the consequences.

Whenever an obsessive thought resurfaces, restate your coping self-talk. Remind yourself of your ability to cope with uncertainty and face your OCD triggers.

Behavioral Restructuring for OCD

Behavioral restructuring or behavior modification focuses on helping individuals with OCD to change if not completely eliminate, their unhelpful and undesirable behaviors (compulsions). Why should you still apply behavioral techniques if you've already addressed your cognitive distortions?

Cognitive restructuring reduces the irrational beliefs and emotional intensity associated with OCD. On the other hand, behavioral techniques directly target the compulsive behaviors associated with OCD.

Thought Stopping, Thought Labeling, and Thought Substitution

Thought Stopping, Thought Labeling, and Thought Substitution are simple techniques that can help you become more aware of your thoughts and how to react to them.

1. **Thought Stopping** is a technique to interrupt or stop intrusive or unwanted thoughts. For example, when you notice an unwanted thought popping up, interrupt your thoughts by shouting "Stop!" mentally or verbally. This will help prevent your thought from spiraling further. (**Tip**: See also DBT's STOP exercise on page 49.)

2. **Thought Labeling** involves giving a name or label to a specific thought or emotion. For example, if you worry excessively about something, you might say, "There goes my OCD worry thought again."

3. **Thought Substitution** involves replacing negative or unhelpful thoughts with more positive or rational ones. That is, when you think of something negative, immediately and consciously replace it with a more balanced and constructive thought. For example, suppose you get an email from your boss asking you to drop by their office before you go home. If your first thought is

that you might get in trouble for making a mistake, tell yourself, "Nope, I could just as well be congratulated for a job well done." Taking this method gives you the power to fight negative thoughts with more logical and positive ones, giving you a healthier and more constructive way of looking at different situations.

Worksheet: What to Do with THOUGHTS

This exercise will help you gain better control over your intrusive thoughts and develop healthier ways of responding to them. Note that applying these three techniques is NOT a requirement. For example, skip Thought Labeling and Thought Substitution if Thought Stopping already works.

1. **Mindful Observation**
    - Find a quiet and comfortable space to sit or lie down.
    - Take a few deep breaths to calm your mind and body.
    - Observe your irrational thoughts without judgment. Let them come and go like clouds passing by.

    If you prefer, you can do any of the DBT Mindfulness exercises instead.

2. **Thought Stopping**
    - As you observe your thoughts, identify a specific intrusive thought related to your OCD. For example, "Did I lock the door?! I'm not sure. Something terrible will happen now!"
    - Mentally shout "**Stop!**" when you notice this thought arising. Picture a big red stop sign in your mind.
    - Take a deep breath and let the thought pass without engaging with it further.

3. **Thought Labeling**
    - Recognize the intrusive thought you just experienced and label it. For example, "Ah, there's my 'did-I-lock-the-door- worry' thought."
    - Remind yourself that this is a thought, not a reflection of reality.

4. **Thought Substitution**

- Identify the negative, irrational, or distorted aspect of your intrusive thought. For example, "I believe something terrible will happen if I forget to lock the door."
- Replace the negative thought with a more balanced and rational one. For example, "Well, I probably DID lock the door. Even if I didn't, it's highly unlikely that something terrible will happen. Unlocked Door=Disaster is not logical. Besides, I can double-check it later if needed."

5. **Journaling**

- Keep a journal to track your progress. Write down the intrusive thoughts you experienced, if and how you used Thought Stopping, Thought Labeling, and Thought Substitution, and how you felt afterwards.
- Reflect on any changes in how you respond to intrusive thoughts over time.

Here's a sample **Thoughts Journal** for you.

THOUGHTS JOURNAL						
Date	What Mindfulness techniques or exercises did I do?	What Thought entered my mind?	Did I do Thought Stopping?	Did I do Thought Labeling?	Did I do Thought Substitution?	Notes:
Example: Feb. 1	*Example: Belly Breathing*	*Example: I'm not good enough for my girlfriend because I think she's taller than me.*	*Example:* ***X***	*Example:*	*Example:* ***X*** *My gf is not taller than me. It's not rational to think she has grown two inches since yesterday.*	*Example: I'm good. I'm okay. I was able to divert my thoughts and not run over to my gf's place and check her height.*

THOUGHTS JOURNAL						
Date	What Mindfulness techniques or exercises did I do?	What Thought entered my mind?	Did I do Thought Stopping?	Did I do Thought Labeling?	Did I do Thought Substitution?	Notes:

Habit Reversal Training (HRT)

Habit Reversal Training (HRT) is a technique that focuses on helping individuals break unwanted habits or repetitive behaviors. In terms of OCD, it is a strategy that will assist you in reversing or unlearning the compulsive habits you've developed in reaction to your obsessions.

Worksheet: Reversing Compulsions

1. **What's your specific compulsive behavior?**

   Example: excessive nail biting

   ____

   ____

   ____

2. **What triggers this compulsive behavior?**

   Example: when I go to school or when I step out of the school bus

   ____

   ____

   ____

3. **Develop a competing response or opposite action.** That is, find a reaction that is physically incompatible with your compulsive behavior.

   Example: place my hands in my pockets

   ____

   ____

   ____

4. **Practice the competing response or opposite action.** Whenever you encounter a trigger, immediately engage in the competing response. Focus on using the competing response every time the trigger occurs.

5. **Track your progress.** Keep a journal to record the instances when you successfully used the competing response and resisted the compulsive behavior. Note the situations, triggers, and feelings you had during these moments. You will likely need to try several conflicting or opposing acts before you find one that works for you. So, please don't be discouraged if you try something that doesn't work. Keep in mind that change takes time, so be patient with yourself!

Here's a sample **Habit Reversal Journal**.

Habit Reversal Journal			
Compulsion	**Trigger**	**Competing Response (Opposite Action)**	**Notes:**
Example: *Excessive nail biting*	*Example:* *When I go to school or when I step out of the school bus*	*Example:* *Place my hands in my pockets*	*Example:* *The first time I tried this, I took my hands immediately out of my pockets and engaged in nail-biting again. But I didn't give up. The next day, I put my hands in my pockets and succeeded more. I actually managed to avoid biting my nails for an entire hour after stepping off the school bus!*

Habit Reversal Journal			
Compulsion	**Trigger**	**Competing Response (Opposite Action)**	**Notes:**

Exposure and Response Prevention (ERP)

Exposure and Response Prevention, or ERP, is considered one of the most effective treatments for OCD. Numerous studies and clinical trials support this[29,30,31], and it's recommended by major mental health organizations, including the American Psychological Association (APA) and the International OCD Foundation (IOCDF).[32,33] As such, we will cover this particular CBT treatment type in more detail.

ERP aims to subject yourself to your OCD trigger slowly and gradually while resisting the urge to perform your compulsions to alleviate the anxiety and distress you feel. If you do the compulsion, you expose yourself to the trigger again.

Important: It's crucial to remember that **trigger exposure should be controlled, gradual, and not overwhelming.** You shouldn't jump into confronting your fears all at once. Instead, the ERP process involves taking small steps and gradually increasing your distress tolerance. This gradual approach is essential because it allows you to build up your ability to handle anxiety without resorting to compulsions. Over time, as you consistently work through trigger exposures, you'll find that your distress tolerance increases while the need to perform compulsions decreases.

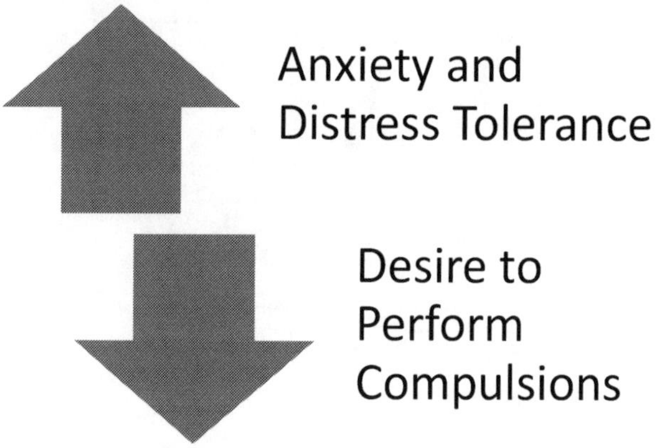

To give you an idea, here's a quick example of how ERP works. (This example is, of course, over-simplified. The ERP exercises in the succeeding pages will provide more guidance and details.)

Trigger: Unsettling sensation that something is "not right"
Obsession: I fear that something bad will happen to me
Compulsion: Petting my cat 15 times from head to tail to feel better
ERP Plan (What to do):

Day 1: Delay holding my cat for 5 minutes.
Day 2: Delay holding my cat for 10 minutes.
Day 3: Delay holding my cat for 15 minutes.
Gradually increase delaying holding my cat until I reach 30 minutes.
Hopefully, by this time, I no longer feel the urge to pet my cat. If not...
Day 4: Delay holding my cat for 30 minutes and pet her only 12 times.
Day 5: Delay holding my cat for 30 minutes and pet her only 10 times.
Gradually decrease the number of times I pet my cat until I no longer have to pet her.

Why is ERP one of the best treatments for OCD?

Apart from the fact that ERP is supported by substantial empirical evidence and has been extensively researched and proven effective in treating OCD, here are the other reasons:

1. **Targets Core Symptoms**

   ERP directly addresses your core symptoms of OCD, which are obsessions and compulsions. By exposing you to your fears (obsessions) and preventing the accompanying compulsive behaviors (compulsions), ERP helps you break the OCD cycle.

2. **Long-Term Benefits**
   ERP focuses on helping you build resilience to distressing thoughts and reduce reliance on compulsions. Unlike short-term relief offered by compulsive behaviors, ERP aims to create lasting changes that can significantly improve OCD symptoms.

3. **Generalizability**
   The skills learned in ERP can be applied to various OCD symptoms and triggers. It's a flexible approach that can be tailored to your specific OCD type. (See What are the Different Types of OCD? on page 17 for a list of OCD types.)

4. **Habituation and Learning**
   Through controlled exposure to feared situations or triggers, you'll gradually experience *habituation*, the natural decrease in anxiety over time. This process helps you learn that your feared consequences are unlikely to occur, reducing the perceived threat and distress.

5. **Helps Prevent Avoidance Behavior**
   ERP challenges avoidance behaviors commonly associated with OCD. By confronting feared situations, ERP encourages you to face your anxieties head-on rather than avoiding them. This diminishes the reinforcement of avoidance behaviors that perpetuate the OCD cycle.

Avoidance Behavior in OCD

Avoidance behavior is a very common coping mechanism for individuals with OCD.[34] For example, a person with an irrational fear of cars and speeding might avoid learning to drive or get into a car. The problem with this type of behavior is that the trigger is never addressed, so the fear is always there.

Avoidance can be physical and mental, and it's often a quick way to feel better when anxious. Unfortunately, over time, avoidance behavior can make OCD symptoms worse.

Here is a quick look at how avoidance behavior develops in people with OCD:

1. **Initial Distress:** Unwanted thoughts and images (obsessions) appear, and these thoughts make you very anxious and uncomfortable. You try to "escape" by avoiding whatever triggers your obsessive thoughts to avoid this distress.
   Example: You get traumatized as a child because you witnessed your grandmother choking to death while eating an apple. This distressing event triggers an irrational fear of apples. As a response, you start avoiding apples altogether to protect yourself from the anxiety and distress you feel when you see them.

2. **Temporary Relief:** When you "avoid," you feel better! But then again, only for a short time.
   Thought: Hmm, see? Removing apples got rid of my anxiety and stress.

3. **Reinforcement:** This temporary relief reinforces the idea that avoidance is an effective coping strategy.
   Thought: Ok, no more applies in the house then.

4. **Negative Reinforcement Loop:** The more you avoid your obsession, the less likely you get the opportunity to get used to the feeling of anxiety when exposed to OCD triggers over time. In the above example, avoiding apples prevents you from getting used to seeing apples. This avoidance keeps you from learning that the bad things you fear are unlikely to happen, keeping the avoidance loop going.

5. **Expansion of Avoidance:** Over time, the scope of your avoidance behavior may worsen. Initially, you may avoid specific situations or triggers directly related to your obsessions. However, as OCD progresses, you may start

avoiding a broader range of situations and activities to prevent triggering your obsessions.
Example: You no longer buy apples. You've forbidden it in your home. But lately, you also seem anxious when you see pears. You want to forbid this in your home too.

6. **Impaired Functioning**: When avoidance behavior worsens, it can significantly impair daily life. You may avoid social events, school or work tasks, and even basic activities necessary for personal well-being.
Example: You no longer want to grocery shop because various fruits trigger you. But then, how will you get groceries? You ask a neighbor to do it for you. At first, they're okay with it, but then they start getting annoyed, and now you're no longer on speaking terms.

   You resort to online shopping. Eventually, you decide not to go out since you can order anything online. This drastically decreases your social circle.

   One day, you're forced to go out. When you do, you realize you're no longer used to dealing with other people, so you self-isolate. Your world becomes smaller and smaller, and you start to develop depression due to your extreme loneliness.

7. **Reinforcement of Obsessions:** Avoidance can strengthen the power of obsessions. The more you avoid certain situations and scenarios, the more important and meaningful your obsessions become, which keeps the OCD cycle going.

8. **Fear of Fear:** Avoidance behavior can create a fear of experiencing fear or anxiety. This fear of fear may lead you to avoid situations where you anticipate potential anxiety. That is, avoidance behavior has made your anxiety and distress tolerance levels so low that you avoid anything and anyone that might make you anxious.

Avoidance, while a natural response to fears and distress, does not address the underlying causes of fears. In the long run, avoiding what triggers anxiety can intensify the fears that fuel OCD symptoms.

---

6. **Collaborative and Gradual Approach**
   ERP is usually done with a trained therapist's help and support. The exposure exercises are presented slowly so you can gain confidence and work at a pace that feels good.

7. **Suitable for Different Severity Levels**
   ERP can be adapted to accommodate varying degrees of OCD severity. It's equally effective for individuals with mild, moderate, or severe OCD symptoms.

8. **Sustainable Self-Management**
   ERP provides skills you can keep using even after therapy is over. This gives you the power to take care of yourself and keep making improvements after treatment is over.

Now that you understand the effectiveness of ERP in OCD treatment, I've provided a dedicated ERP worksheet for each OCD type (page 17) mentioned in this book. These worksheets will help you apply ERP techniques and challenge your OCD-related thoughts in a structured and manageable way.

If you have Contamination OCD, please do the ERP worksheet on page 119.
If you have Checking OCD, please do the ERP worksheet on page 124.
If you have Symmetry and Odering OCD, please do the ERP worksheet on page 130.
If you have Hoarding OCD, please do the ERP worksheet on page 135.
If you have Intrusive Thoughts OCD, please do the ERP worksheet on page 141.
If you have Just-Right OCD, please do the ERP worksheet on page 146.

As previously mentioned, experiencing multiple types of OCD is entirely possible. I recommend starting with the ERP exercise related to your least distressing OCD type. By tackling the least distressing OCD type first, you can gradually build confidence and develop skills to manage other OCD manifestations effectively.

I've shared with you that I suffer from *Checking*, *Intrusive Thoughts*, and *Just-Right OCD*. So, personally, I did the ERP exercise for *Intrusive Thoughts* first, followed by the one for *Checking*, and did the worksheet for *Just-Right OCD* last. This is because I find dealing with my *Just-Right OCD* the most challenging.

Safety First: Remember that ERP aims to help you face your specific OCD triggers (exposure) while resisting compulsive behaviors (response prevention). Also, as mentioned above, ERP is usually done in collaboration with a trained therapist, so please be careful and mindful when doing any of the exercises below. I strongly suggest you **identify someone you trust or have the number of a trained professional before doing any of the succeeding exercises**. DO NOT hesitate to reach out to this person whenever you feel overwhelmed.

Worksheet: ERP Exercise for Contamination OCD

Step 1. Identify Your OCD Triggers

Make a list of specific triggers that provoke your Contamination-related obsessions and compulsions. Following are some possible triggers. Check the ones that apply to you. Please add more if you don't see your specific trigger.

- ☐ Touching doorknobs, handles, or other public surfaces.
- ☐ Being in crowded places or public transportation.
- ☐ Contact with bodily fluids or waste.
- ☐ Exposure to dirt or germs.
- ☐ Handling money or shared objects.
- ☐ Others:

  ____

  ____

  ____

Step 2. Create an Exposure Hierarchy

Arrange the triggers from least distressing (lowest number) to most distressing (highest number), creating a personal exposure hierarchy. For example:

Anxiety Trigger	Example Rating	Your Rating
Touching doorknobs, handles, or other public surfaces.	*3*	
Being in crowded places or public transportation.	*1*	
Contact with bodily fluids or waste.	*5*	
Exposure to dirt or germs.	*2*	
Handling money or shared objects.	*4*	
Other triggers:		

In this example, *being in crowded places or on public transportation* is the least distressing, while *contact with bodily fluids or waste* causes the most or maximum distress.

Step 3. Plan Exposure Strategies

- Beginning with the least distressing trigger from your exposure hierarchy, write down how you will slowly and gradually expose yourself to it.
- Practice Radical Acceptance (page 33) here. Accept that this process will most likely cause temporary discomfort but will ultimately reduce your anxiety and weaken its grip on you over time.
- Purposefully expose yourself to the least distressing trigger **without** engaging in any compulsive behaviors or rituals.

Following are **Exposure Strategy examples related to Contamination OCD**. You don't need to try them all or in any particular order. Go over the list and select which strategy(ies) you want to use on your least distressing trigger.

Important: The specific amount of time and frequency you spend for each exposure exercise depends on your personal goals, the severity of your OCD symptoms, and your current distress tolerance levels. In some circumstances, exposures may last only a few minutes, while others may last much longer. The frequency of exposures can range from everyday to a few times per week.

☐ **Imaginary Exposure**: Create scenarios where you encounter "contaminated" situations. Practice tolerating the anxiety without engaging in rituals or avoidance.

☐ **Avoidance Reduction**: Gradually reduce avoidance behaviors related to contamination fears. For example, if you avoid certain rooms or areas, expose yourself to those spaces without excessive cleaning.

☐ **Media Exposure**: Watch videos or read articles related to germs or contamination. Resist the urge to seek reassurance or wash hands immediately afterwards.

- ☐ **Public Spaces Exposure:** Spend time in public places, such as parks, coffee shops, or grocery stores, without avoiding contact with surfaces. Resist the urge to wash hands immediately afterwards.
- ☐ **Gradual Touching:** Touch a doorknob or handle and refrain from immediately washing or using hand sanitizer. Gradually increase the duration before washing.
- ☐ **Handling "Contaminated" Objects**: Touch objects you perceive as contaminated and resist your compulsions, such as avoiding touching other items afterward or washing hands excessively.
- ☐ **Cross-Contamination Challenge**: Deliberately touch a "contaminated" surface and then touch other objects without washing. Challenge the belief that contamination spreads easily.
- ☐ **Resisting Handwashing Rituals**: Delay handwashing by a few minutes each time you feel the urge to wash. Use Mindfulness (page 38) and Distress Tolerance (page 45) techniques to sit with the discomfort.

Step 4. Exposure and Mindfulness

Expose yourself to the trigger using the strategy you chose in Step #3 above. Throughout the exposure, practice Mindfulness (page 38). Observe and accept any anxiety or discomfort you experience without judgment.

Step 5. Apply Distress Tolerance Skills

- At the first onset of anxiety or distress, apply your Distress Tolerance training (page 45).
- **Stay in the situation** or with the trigger until your anxiety decreases naturally. Avoid rushing or escaping the situation prematurely. There is no set time limit here, as it depends on factors such as the severity of your anxiety, the trigger to which you're exposing yourself, and your personal progress in managing your distress.

Step 6. Resist Compulsions

Do your best to refrain from engaging in any compulsions or rituals, even if the anxiety feels intense. Remind yourself that compulsions only provide temporary relief and reinforce OCD patterns.

Tip: Do Check the Facts (page 65) or What to Do with THOUGHTS (page 104).

Step 7. Record Your Experience

Keep a journal to document your thoughts, feelings, and level of anxiety during the exposure. Note any changes in anxiety levels over time. (See sample Exposure and Response Journal on page 170170.)

Step 8. Gradual Progression

- Gradually work your way up your exposure hierarchy, tackling more distressing triggers one by one.
- As you gain confidence and experience success with each exposure, you'll find the anxiety decreasing and your ability to manage OCD symptoms improving.

Step 9. Self-Compassion

ERP is difficult, as you deliberately expose yourself to anxiety and distress. As such, treating yourself with patience, kindness, and understanding is important. Also, remind yourself that anxiety is a natural response to facing fears. It's okay to feel anxious; it doesn't mean you're failing at ERP. Just keep on trying. Remember, each attempt means progress.

Step 10. Address the Next Trigger

- Go back to Step #2 – Exposure Hierarchy.
- Select the next OCD trigger to address.
- Repeat steps 3-9 until you address all your OCD triggers.

Worksheet: ERP Exercise for Checking OCD

Step 1. Identify Your OCD Triggers

Make a list of specific triggers that provoke your Checking-related obsessions and compulsions. Following are some possible triggers. Check the ones that apply to you. Please add more if you don't see your specific trigger.

- ☐ Leaving the house (e.g., checking if the door is locked, the stove is turned off, the tap is not leaking, etc.).
- ☐ Fear of causing harm to others (e.g., checking if a loved one is safe).
- ☐ Doubt about completing tasks (e.g., checking if emails were sent, homework was completed, etc.).
- ☐ Fear of making mistakes (e.g., checking documents repeatedly for errors, writing, reading, and re-writing emails before sending them, etc.).
- ☐ Concern about accidents (e.g., checking if lights or appliances are off, leaving meetings to check if the car door is locked, etc.).
- ☐ Others:

  ____

  ____

  ____

Step 2. Create an Exposure Hierarchy

Arrange the triggers from least distressing (lowest number) to most distressing (highest number), creating a personal exposure hierarchy. For example:

Anxiety Trigger	***Example Rating***	**Your Rating**
Leaving the house (e.g., checking if the door is locked, the stove is turned off, the tap is not leaking, etc.).	*5*	
Fear of causing harm to others (e.g., checking if a loved one is safe).	*1*	
Doubt about completing tasks (e.g., checking if emails were sent, homework was completed, etc.).	*2*	
Fear of making mistakes (e.g., checking documents repeatedly for errors, writing, reading, and re-writing emails before sending them, etc.).	*3*	
Concern about accidents (e.g., checking if lights or appliances are off, leaving meetings to check if the car door is locked, etc.).	*4*	
Other triggers:		

In this example, *fear of causing harm to others* is the least distressing, while *leaving the house* causes the most or maximum distress.

Step 3. Plan Exposure Strategies

- Beginning with the least distressing trigger from your exposure hierarchy, write down how you will slowly and gradually expose yourself to it.
- Practice Radical Acceptance (page 33) here. Accept that this process will most likely cause temporary discomfort but will ultimately reduce your anxiety and weaken its grip on you over time.
- Purposefully expose yourself to the trigger **without** engaging in any compulsive behaviors or rituals.

Following are **Exposure Strategy examples related to Checking OCD**. You don't need to try them all or in any particular order. See which options appeal to you most.

Important: The specific amount of time and frequency you spend for each exposure exercise depends on your personal goals, the severity of your OCD symptoms, and your current distress tolerance levels. In some circumstances, exposures may last only a few minutes, while others may last much longer. The frequency of exposures can range from everyday to a few times per week.

- ☐ **Delayed Checking:** Practice delaying the checking ritual by a few minutes each time you feel the urge. Gradually increase the delay to challenge the need for immediate reassurance.
- ☐ **Contingency Management:** Set specific rules for checking, such as "I will only check once and move on." Avoid going back to check again.
- ☐ **Item Arrangement:** Purposefully arrange items in a different order than usual and resist the compulsion to rearrange them.

☐ **Incompleteness Tolerance:** Deliberately leave tasks partially undone and practice tolerating the discomfort without giving in to checking compulsions.

☐ **Leaving the House:** Leave the house without checking everything multiple times. Use a checklist to reassure yourself that you completed essential tasks before leaving.

☐ **Digital Checking Challenge:** Limit checking emails, messages, or social media notifications to specific times of the day. Gradually reduce the frequency of checking. For example, check your messages only once in the morning and once in the evening.

☐ **Experiment with Memory:** Challenge the belief that your memory is unreliable. Refrain from checking and trust that you completed tasks as usual.

☐ **Intentional Errors:** Intentionally introduce minor errors into your work or tasks and resist the urge to correct them immediately.

☐ **Purposefully Leave Items Behind:** Leave items behind intentionally, such as your phone or wallet, and practice accepting the discomfort without returning to check.

Step 4. Exposure and Mindfulness

Expose yourself to the trigger using the strategy you chose in Step #3 above. Throughout the exposure, practice Mindfulness (page 38). Observe and accept any anxiety or discomfort you experience without judgment.

Step 5. Apply Distress Tolerance Skills

- At the first onset of anxiety or distress, apply your Distress Tolerance training (page 45).

- **Stay in the situation** or with the trigger until your anxiety decreases naturally. Avoid rushing or escaping the situation prematurely. There is no set time limit here, as it depends on factors such as the severity of your anxiety, the trigger to which you're exposing yourself, and your personal progress in managing your distress.

Step 6. Resist Compulsions

Do your best to refrain from engaging in any compulsions or rituals, even if the anxiety feels intense. Remind yourself that compulsions only provide temporary relief and reinforce OCD patterns.

Tip: Do Check the Facts (page 65) or What to Do with THOUGHTS (page 104).

Step 7. Record Your Experience

Keep a journal to document your thoughts, feelings, and level of anxiety during the exposure. Note any changes in anxiety levels over time. (See sample Exposure and Response Journal on page 170.)

Step 8. Gradual Progression

- Gradually work your way up your exposure hierarchy, tackling more distressing triggers one by one.
- As you gain confidence and experience success with each exposure, you'll find the anxiety decreasing and your ability to manage OCD symptoms improving.

Step 9. Self-Compassion

ERP is difficult because you're deliberately exposing yourself to anxiety and distress. As such, treating yourself with patience, kindness, and understanding is important. Also, remind yourself that anxiety is a natural response to facing fears.

It's okay to feel anxious; it doesn't mean you're failing at ERP. Just keep on trying. Remember, each attempt means progress.

Step 10. Address the Next Trigger

- Go back to Step #2 – Exposure Hierarchy.
- Select the next OCD trigger to address.
- Repeat steps 3-9 until you address all your OCD triggers.

Worksheet: ERP Exercise for Symmetry and Ordering OCD

Step 1. Identify Your OCD Triggers

Make a list of specific triggers that provoke your Symmetry and Ordering-related obsessions compulsions. Following are some possible triggers. Check the ones that apply to you. Please add more if you don't see your specific trigger.

- ☐ Seeing asymmetrical or disorganized objects or arrangements.
- ☐ Fear of something terrible happening if objects are not in perfect order.
- ☐ Feeling anxious when things are not arranged or organized symmetrically.
- ☐ The need to arrange objects in specific patterns to prevent harm or bad luck.
- ☐ Obsession with evenness, exactness, or precision in daily routines.
- ☐ Others:

  ____

  ____

  ____

Step 2. Create an Exposure Hierarchy

Arrange the triggers from least distressing (lowest number) to most distressing (highest number), creating a personal exposure hierarchy. For example:

Anxiety Trigger	*Example Rating*	Your Rating
Seeing asymmetrical or disorganized objects or arrangements.	*1*	
Fear of something terrible happening if objects are not in perfect order.	*5*	
Feeling anxious when things are not arranged or organized symmetrically.	*3*	
The need to arrange objects in specific patterns to prevent harm or bad luck.	*4*	
Obsession with evenness, exactness, or precision in daily routines.	*2*	
Other triggers:		

In this example, *seeing asymmetrical or disorganized objects or arrangements* is the least distressing, while *fear of something terrible happening if objects are not in perfect order* causes the most or maximum distress.

Step 3. Plan Exposure Strategies

- Beginning with the least distressing trigger from your exposure hierarchy, write down how you will slowly and gradually expose yourself to it.
- Practice Radical Acceptance (page 33) here. Accept that this process will most likely cause temporary discomfort but will ultimately reduce your anxiety and weaken its grip on you over time.
- Purposefully expose yourself to the trigger **without** engaging in any compulsive behaviors or rituals.

Following are **Exposure Strategy examples related to Symmetry and Ordering OCD**. You don't need to try them all or in any particular order. See which options appeal to you most.

Important: The specific amount of time and frequency you spend for each exposure exercise depends on your personal goals, the severity of your OCD symptoms, and your current distress tolerance levels. In some circumstances, exposures may last only a few minutes, while others may last much longer. The frequency of exposures can range from everyday to a few times per week.

- ☐ **Imaginary Exposure:** Practice visualizing asymmetrical or disordered arrangements and staying calm despite discomfort.
- ☐ **Asymmetrical Patterns:** Set up (or ask someone to set up) asymmetrical patterns or arrangements and practice tolerating the discomfort without altering them.
- ☐ **Mixed Patterns:** Mix different patterns or orders when arranging objects, challenging the need for everything to be symmetrical.

- ☐ **Unordered Spaces:** Designate certain spaces or areas as deliberately unordered and resist the compulsion to organize them.
- ☐ **Disorderly Arrangements:** Purposefully create disorderly arrangements of objects and resist the compulsion to rearrange them symmetrically.
- ☐ **Break Routines:** Intentionally break established routines and allow yourself to deviate from symmetrical or ordered behaviors.
- ☐ **Introduce Variety:** Introduce variety into your daily routines, such as using different colors or sizes for objects you typically arrange symmetrically.
- ☐ **Accept Imperfections:** Intentionally create imperfect or slightly disorderly arrangements and practice accepting the imperfections without correcting them.
- ☐ **Time Limits:** Set time limits for arranging or ordering tasks. When the time is up, move on *without* further adjustments.

Step 4. Exposure and Mindfulness

Expose yourself to the trigger using the strategy you chose in Step #3 above. Throughout the exposure, practice Mindfulness (page 38). Observe and accept any anxiety or discomfort you experience without judgment.

Step 5. Apply Distress Tolerance Skills

- At the first onset of anxiety or distress, apply your Distress Tolerance training (page 45).
- **Stay in the situation** or with the trigger until your anxiety decreases naturally. Avoid rushing or escaping the situation prematurely. There is no set time limit here, as it depends on factors such as the severity of your anxiety, the trigger to which you're exposing yourself, and your personal progress in managing your distress.

Resist Compulsions

Do your best to refrain from engaging in any compulsions or rituals, even if the anxiety feels intense. Remind yourself that compulsions only provide temporary relief and reinforce OCD patterns.

Tip: Do Check the Facts (page 65) or What to Do with THOUGHTS (page 104).

Step 6. Record Your Experience

Keep a journal to document your thoughts, feelings, and level of anxiety during the exposure. Note any changes in anxiety levels over time. (See sample Exposure and Response Journal on page 170.)

Step 7. Gradual Progression

- Gradually work your way up your exposure hierarchy, tackling more distressing triggers one by one.
- As you gain confidence and experience success with each exposure, you'll find the anxiety decreasing and your ability to manage OCD symptoms improving.

Step 8. Self-Compassion

ERP is difficult because you're deliberately exposing yourself to anxiety and distress. As such, treating yourself with patience, kindness, and understanding is important. Also, remind yourself that anxiety is a natural response to facing fears. It's okay to feel anxious; it doesn't mean you're failing at ERP. Just keep on trying. Remember, each attempt means progress.

Step 9. Address the Next Trigger

- Go back to Step #2 – Exposure Hierarchy.
- Select the next OCD trigger to address.
- Repeat steps 3-9 until you address all your OCD triggers.

Worksheet: ERP Exercise for Hoarding OCD

Step 1. Identify Your OCD Triggers

Make a list of specific triggers that provoke your Hoarding-related and compulsions. Following are some possible triggers. Check the ones that apply to you. Please add more if you don't see your specific trigger.

- ☐ Fear of losing important items or sentimental possessions.
- ☐ Anxiety about discarding things due to perceived future use or value.
- ☐ Difficulty deciding which items to keep or throw away.
- ☐ Emotional attachment to possessions, even those with no practical use.
- ☐ Concerns about making the wrong decision regarding disposal.
- ☐ Others:

  ____

  ____

  ____

Step 2. Create an Exposure Hierarchy

Arrange the triggers from least distressing (lowest number) to most distressing (highest number), creating a personal exposure hierarchy. For example:

Anxiety Trigger	*Example Rating*	Your Rating
Fear of losing important items or sentimental possessions.	*2*	
Anxiety about discarding things due to perceived future use or value.	*3*	
Difficulty deciding which items to keep or throw away.	*4*	
Emotional attachment to possessions, even those with no practical use.	*5*	
Concerns about making the wrong decision regarding disposal.	*1*	
Other triggers:		

In this example, *concerns about making the wrong decision* are the least distressing, while *emotional attachment to possessions, even those with no practical use,* causes the most or maximum distress.

Step 3. Plan Exposure Strategies

- Beginning with the least distressing trigger from your exposure hierarchy, write down how you will slowly and gradually expose yourself to it.
- Practice Radical Acceptance (page 33) here. Accept that this process will most likely cause temporary discomfort but will ultimately reduce your anxiety and weaken its grip on you over time.
- Purposefully expose yourself to the trigger **without** engaging in any compulsive behaviors or rituals.

Following are **Exposure Strategy examples related to Hoarding OCD**. You don't need to try them all or in any particular order. See which options appeal to you most.

Important: The specific amount of time and frequency you spend for each exposure exercise depends on your personal goals, the severity of your OCD symptoms, and your current distress tolerance levels. In some circumstances, exposures may last only a few minutes, while others may last much longer. The frequency of exposures can range from everyday to a few times per week.

- ☐ **Imaginary Exposure**: Imagine getting rid of certain possessions or decluttering spaces in your mind. Observe any anxious feelings and practice letting go of the attachment.
- ☐ **Avoid Acquiring New Items:** Refrain from acquiring new possessions impulsively. Practice mindful purchasing and question whether new items are essential.

- ☐ **Photographic Memory:** Take photographs of sentimental possessions and rely on the pictures for emotional connection rather than keeping the physical items.
- ☐ **Experiment with Letting Go:** Try parting with items briefly, such as storing them away for a week. Observe your feelings during this time and evaluate if you genuinely need them back.
- ☐ **One Item at a Time:** Focus on one item at a time and decide whether to keep, donate, or discard it. Resist the temptation to keep everything.
- ☐ **Controlled Decluttering:** Choose a small area or category of items to declutter. Set a time limit for decluttering and stick to it, even if it feels uncomfortable.
- ☐ **Selective Discarding:** Gradually discard items with less emotional value or limited practical use. Practice resisting the urge to keep them.
- ☐ **Exposure to Emptiness:** Create or view a decluttered space and sit with the feelings of emptiness or loss that may arise.
- ☐ **Seek Support:** Involve a trusted friend or family member in decluttering to provide support and encouragement.

Step 4. Exposure and Mindfulness

Expose yourself to the trigger using the strategy you chose in Step #3 above. Throughout the exposure, practice Mindfulness (page 38). Observe and accept any anxiety or discomfort you experience without judgment.

Step 5. Apply Distress Tolerance Skills

- At the first onset of anxiety or distress, apply your Distress Tolerance training (page 45).

- **Stay in the situation** or with the trigger until your anxiety decreases naturally. Avoid rushing or escaping the situation prematurely. There is no set time limit here, as it depends on factors such as the severity of your anxiety, the trigger to which you're exposing yourself, and your personal progress in managing your distress.

Step 6. Resist Compulsions

Do your best to refrain from engaging in any compulsions or rituals, even if the anxiety feels intense. Remind yourself that compulsions only provide temporary relief and reinforce OCD patterns.

Tip: Do Check the Facts (page 65) or What to Do with THOUGHTS (page 104).

Step 7. Record Your Experience

Keep a journal to document your thoughts, feelings, and level of anxiety during the exposure. Note any changes in anxiety levels over time. (See sample Exposure and Response Journal on page 170.)

Step 8. Gradual Progression

- Gradually work your way up your exposure hierarchy, tackling more distressing triggers one by one.
- As you gain confidence and experience success with each exposure, you'll find the anxiety decreasing and your ability to manage OCD symptoms improving.

Step 9. Self-Compassion

ERP is difficult because you're deliberately exposing yourself to anxiety and distress. As such, treating yourself with patience, kindness, and understanding is important. Also, remind yourself that anxiety is a natural response to facing fears.

It's okay to feel anxious; it doesn't mean you're failing at ERP. Just keep on trying. Remember, each attempt means progress.

Step 10. Address the Next Trigger

- Go back to Step #2 – Exposure Hierarchy.
- Select the next OCD trigger to address.
- Repeat steps 3-9 until you address all your OCD triggers.

Worksheet: ERP Exercise for Intrusive Thoughts OCD

Content Warning: harmful thoughts, violence, immorality, and others.

Step 1. Identify Your OCD Triggers

Make a list of specific triggers that provoke your Intrusive Thoughts-related, obsessions and compulsions. Following are some possible triggers. Check the ones that apply to you. Please add more if you don't see your specific trigger.

- ☐ Violent or aggressive thoughts about harming oneself or others (e.g., thinking of stabbing yourself or a loved one with a knife).
- ☐ Fear of engaging in morally or socially unacceptable behaviors (e.g., cheating, stealing, etc.).
- ☐ Unwanted sexual thoughts that are distressing or contrary to one's values (e.g., engaging in sex with the opposite sex).
- ☐ Intrusive blasphemous or heretical thoughts conflicting with one's religious beliefs (e.g., thinking of engaging and winning a debate with God).
- ☐ Disturbing or taboo thoughts that evoke intense anxiety or guilt (e.g., thinking life is better without your newborn).
- ☐ Others:

  ____

  ____

  ____

Step 2. Create an Exposure Hierarchy

Arrange the triggers from least distressing (lowest number) to most distressing (highest number), creating a personal exposure hierarchy. For example:

Anxiety Trigger	*Example Rating*	Your Rating
Violent or aggressive thoughts about harming oneself or others	*5*	
Fear of engaging in morally or socially unacceptable behaviors	*1*	
Unwanted sexual thoughts that are distressing or contrary to one's values	*2*	
Intrusive blasphemous thoughts conflicting with one's religious beliefs	*3*	
Disturbing or taboo thoughts that evoke intense anxiety or guilt	*4*	
Other triggers:		

In this example, *fear of engaging in morally or socially unacceptable behaviors* is the least distressing, while *violent or aggressive thoughts about harming oneself or others* cause the most or maximum distress.

Step 3. Plan Exposure Strategies

- Beginning with the least distressing trigger from your exposure hierarchy, write down how you will slowly and gradually expose yourself to it.
- Practice Radical Acceptance (page 33) here. Accept that this process will most likely cause temporary discomfort but will ultimately reduce your anxiety and weaken its grip on you over time.
- Purposefully expose yourself to the trigger **without** engaging in any compulsive behaviors or rituals.

Following are **Exposure Strategy examples related to Intrusive Thoughts OCD**. You don't need to try them all or in any particular order. See which options appeal to you most.

Important: The specific amount of time and frequency you spend for each exposure exercise depends on your personal goals, the severity of your OCD symptoms, and your current distress tolerance levels. In some circumstances, exposures may last only a few minutes, while others may last much longer. The frequency of exposures can range from everyday to a few times per week.

- ☐ **Humor Exposure:** Create humorous and exaggerated versions of intrusive thoughts. Laugh at the absurdity of the thoughts to diminish their power.
- ☐ **Exposure to Trigger Words or Phrases:** Write down trigger words or phrases associated with intrusive thoughts. Gradually expose yourself to them without engaging in rituals or avoiding them.
- ☐ **Thought Labeling:** Label intrusive thoughts as "OCD thoughts" when they arise, reminding yourself that they are a product of your condition and NOT reflective of your true self.

- ☐ **Thought Repetition:** Repeat the intrusive thought deliberately in your mind. This exposure reduces the perceived power of the thought over time.
- ☐ **Scripted Imaginal Exposure:** Write a detailed script describing a distressing, intrusive thought. Read the script repeatedly without attempting to suppress or avoid the thoughts.
- ☐ **Exposure to Moral Dilemmas:** Engage in scenarios that involve moral dilemmas related to your intrusive thoughts. Resist the urge to solve the dilemma through rituals.
- ☐ **Thought Acceptance:** Accept that intrusive thoughts are a natural part of the human experience and may not have any significance.
- ☐ **Response Prevention:** Refrain from engaging in mental rituals or compulsive behaviors in response to intrusive thoughts.
- ☐ **Group Exposure:** Share your intrusive thoughts with a supportive and understanding group. Realize that others may experience similar thoughts, reducing feelings of isolation and shame.

Step 4. Exposure and Mindfulness

Expose yourself to the trigger using the strategy you chose in Step #3 above. Throughout the exposure, practice Mindfulness (page 38). Observe and accept any anxiety or discomfort you experience without judgment.

Step 5. Apply Distress Tolerance Skills

- At the first onset of anxiety or distress, apply your Distress Tolerance training (page 45).
- **Stay in the situation** or with the trigger until your anxiety decreases naturally. Avoid rushing or escaping the situation prematurely. There is no set time limit here, as it depends on factors such as the severity of your anxiety, the trigger to which you're exposing yourself, and your personal progress in managing your distress.

Step 6. Resist Compulsions

Do your best to refrain from engaging in any compulsions or rituals, even if the anxiety feels intense. Remind yourself that compulsions only provide temporary relief and reinforce OCD patterns.

Tip: Do Check the Facts (page 65) or What to Do with THOUGHTS (page 104).

Step 7. Record Your Experience

Keep a journal to document your thoughts, feelings, and level of anxiety during the exposure. Note any changes in anxiety levels over time. (See sample Exposure and Response Journal on page 170.)

Step 8. Gradual Progression

- Gradually work your way up your exposure hierarchy, tackling more distressing triggers one by one.
- As you gain confidence and experience success with each exposure, you'll find the anxiety decreasing and your ability to manage OCD symptoms improving.

Step 9. Self-Compassion

ERP is difficult because you're deliberately exposing yourself to anxiety and distress. As such, treating yourself with patience, kindness, and understanding is important. Also, remind yourself that anxiety is a natural response to facing fears. It's okay to feel anxious; it doesn't mean you're failing at ERP. Just keep on trying. Remember, each attempt means progress.

Step 10. Address the Next Trigger

- Go back to Step #2 – Exposure Hierarchy.
- Select the next OCD trigger to address.
- Repeat steps 3-9 until you address all your OCD triggers.

Worksheet: ERP Exercise for Just-Right OCD

Step 1. Identify Your OCD Triggers

Make a list of specific triggers that provoke your Just-Right-related obsessions and compulsions. Following are some possible triggers. Check the ones that apply to you. Please add more if you don't see your specific trigger.

- ☐ Unsettling sensations that something is not in the right place or position.
- ☐ The need for objects or arrangements to be perfectly aligned or symmetrical.
- ☐ Uncomfortable feelings of incompleteness or dissatisfaction until things feel "just right."
- ☐ Fear of negative consequences if things are not arranged or completed in a specific way.
- ☐ Overwhelming anxiety when unable to achieve the desired sense of completion or perfection.
- ☐ Others:

  ____

  ____

  ____

Step 2. Create an Exposure Hierarchy

Arrange the triggers from least distressing (lowest number) to most distressing (highest number), creating a personal exposure hierarchy. For example:

Anxiety Trigger	*Example Rating*	Your Rating
Unsettling sensations that something is not in the right place or position.	*2*	
The need for objects or arrangements to be perfectly aligned or symmetrical.	*1*	
Uncomfortable feelings of incompleteness or dissatisfaction until things feel "just right."	*3*	
Fear of negative consequences if things are not arranged or completed in a specific way.	*4*	
Overwhelming anxiety when unable to achieve the desired sense of completion or perfection.	*5*	
Other triggers:		

In this example, *unsettling sensations that something is not in the right place or position* is the least distressing, while *overwhelming anxiety when unable to achieve the desired sense of completion or perfection* causes the most or maximum distress.

Step 3. Plan Exposure Strategies

- Beginning with the least distressing trigger from your exposure hierarchy, write down how you will slowly and gradually expose yourself to it.
- Practice Radical Acceptance (page 33) here. Accept that this process will most likely cause temporary discomfort but will ultimately reduce your anxiety and weaken its grip on you over time.
- Purposefully expose yourself to the trigger **without** engaging in any compulsive behaviors or rituals.

Following are **Exposure Strategy examples related to Just-Right OCD**. You don't need to try them all or in any particular order. See which options appeal to you most.

Important: The specific amount of time and frequency you spend for each exposure exercise depends on your personal goals, the severity of your OCD symptoms, and your current distress tolerance levels. In some circumstances, exposures may last only a few minutes, while others may last much longer. The frequency of exposures can range from everyday to a few times per week.

☐ **Disorderly Arrangements:** Purposefully arrange objects in a slightly disordered or asymmetrical manner. Practice resisting the compulsion to rearrange them until they feel "just right."

☐ **Imperfect Alignment:** Allow objects to be imperfectly aligned or positioned without correcting them to your desired level of precision.

- ☐ **Break Symmetry:** Intentionally create asymmetrical arrangements and refrain from adjusting them to feel balanced.
- ☐ **Leave Things Incomplete:** Start tasks or projects and leave them partially undone without the need to complete them immediately.
- ☐ **Delayed Adjustment:** If you feel the urge to adjust something, delay the action for a few minutes or set a specific time later.
- ☐ **Incompleteness Tolerance:** Challenge the belief that things must feel complete to be acceptable. Embrace the feeling of incompleteness without trying to alleviate it.
- ☐ **Variety in Arrangements:** Introduce variety in arranging objects or performing routines, resisting the need for a specific pattern.
- ☐ **Exposure to Dissatisfaction:** Engage in activities where you deliberately accept the feeling of dissatisfaction or imperfection.

Step 4. Exposure and Mindfulness

Expose yourself to the trigger using the strategy you chose in Step #3 above. Throughout the exposure, practice Mindfulness (page 38). Observe and accept any anxiety or discomfort you experience without judgment.

Step 5. Apply Distress Tolerance Skills

- At the first onset of anxiety or distress, apply your Distress Tolerance training (page 45).
- **Stay in the situation** or with the trigger until your anxiety decreases naturally. Avoid rushing or escaping the situation prematurely. There is no set time limit here, as it depends on factors such as the severity of your anxiety, the trigger to which you're exposing yourself, and your personal progress in managing your distress.

Step 6. Resist Compulsions

Do your best to refrain from engaging in any compulsions or rituals, even if the anxiety feels intense. Remind yourself that compulsions only provide temporary relief and reinforce OCD patterns.

Tip: Do Check the Facts (page 65) or What to Do with THOUGHTS (page 104).

Step 7. Record Your Experience

Keep a journal to document your thoughts, feelings, and level of anxiety during the exposure. Note any changes in anxiety levels over time. (See sample Exposure and Response Journal on page 170.)

Step 8. Gradual Progression

- Gradually work your way up your exposure hierarchy, tackling more distressing triggers one by one.
- As you gain confidence and experience success with each exposure, you'll find the anxiety decreasing and your ability to manage OCD symptoms improving.

Step 9. Self-Compassion

ERP is difficult because you're deliberately exposing yourself to anxiety and distress. As such, treating yourself with patience, kindness, and understanding is important. Also, remind yourself that anxiety is a natural response to facing fears. It's okay to feel anxious; it doesn't mean you're failing at ERP. Just keep on trying. Remember, each attempt means progress.

Step 10. Address the Next Trigger

- Go back to Step #2 – Exposure Hierarchy.
- Select the next OCD trigger to address.
- Repeat steps 3-9 until you address all your OCD triggers.

Strategies for OCD Relapse Prevention

"Relapse doesn't mean you've lost all your progress. It's a reminder that healing is a continuous process that requires self-compassion and perseverance."
– Dr. Sue Varma

OCD is a chronic condition, so long-term management is essential to maintain treatment gains and prevent relapse. Otherwise, OCD symptoms may return or worsen, especially when treatment is discontinued prematurely, when individuals face significant stressors, or when comorbidity with another mental health disorder exists. However, this does not mean that relapse is inevitable. You can prevent relapse. One of the secrets is to be vigilant and address any resurgence of OCD symptoms promptly.

Identifying Early Warning Signs of Relapse

It's important to recognize the early signs of a possible return of OCD symptoms if you want to keep progressing in your treatment. Here are some of the things you might want to keep an eye on.

External factors. Pay attention to external factors that might increase stress or anxiety, such as significant life changes, work demands, or relationship issues.

Physical signs. Notice any physical sensations or changes accompanying heightened anxiety, such as increased heart rate, muscle tension, or difficulty sleeping.

Thought patterns. Be mindful of intrusive, irrational or obsessive thoughts that may be resurfacing. For example, you suddenly start to think about something (e.g., an object, person, activity, situation, etc.) more than usual.

Emotional shifts or sudden mood changes. Track your emotional well-being. Are you feeling more irritable, overwhelmed, or emotionally sensitive?

Social withdrawal Pay attention to any tendencies to withdraw from social interactions or hobbies you once enjoyed.

Return of OCD patterns. One of the advantages of undergoing OCD treatment is getting to know OCD and its effects on you better. For example, you're not guessing what's possibly triggering you—you know. You know, you're not wondering what you might do when you experience OCD-induced anxiety and distress. As such, it's important to reflect on past experiences and identify patterns that tend to precede a worsening of OCD symptoms.

For example: Say you have contamination OCD and your specific compulsion is washing your hands for extended periods. Thanks to ERP, you've completely addressed this compulsion. However, a significant life event occurred (e.g., divorce, death of a loved one, job relocation, etc.), and you find yourself washing your hands for an extended period in the bathroom. In this situation, immediately apply what helped you before to prevent the complete relapse of OCD symptoms.

Despite your best efforts and intentions, it's still possible to experience an OCD relapse, and it's okay to fear this. This is a natural reaction. However, I've found that Radical Acceptance (page 33) works better. So, instead of being afraid of relapse, I accepted the likelihood that it would occur.

I tell myself a sample Radical Acceptance statement: *Even though OCD relapse can be distressing and challenging, I radically accept that it is a part of my journey. Setbacks happen in many areas of life, not just OCD, and it's okay to experience moments of struggle. If and when an OCD relapse occurs, I'll show myself compassion and understanding. Instead of dwelling on frustration or self-criticism, I'll seek support, recommit to my treatment, and learn from the experience. Relapse does not define me; it's an opportunity for growth and strengthening my resilience.*

I encourage you to write your own Radical Acceptance statement below.

____

____

____

____

____

____

I find this step empowering because I no longer "dread" relapse. I can move on to ways to prevent it.

Top 10 Ways to Prevent OCD Relapse

Here, we'll discuss important ways to keep the progress you've made in dealing with OCD. Even though OCD can be hard to deal with, effective ways to avoid relapsing can greatly reduce the chance of doing so. These tried-and-true methods are meant to give you the information and skills to handle potential triggers and setbacks confidently. Now, let's dive into these helpful tips and find out how to deal with OCD in the long run.

1. Set Realistic Goals

Set achievable goals for yourself in managing OCD. Focus on small goals and celebrate progress, regardless of how "small" they may seem. Don't put too much pressure on yourself as well. Otherwise, anxiety might set in and trigger OCD symptoms. Examples of small, realistic goals: Getting better at accepting uncertainty in daily situations, adopting mindfulness habits daily, being more sociable, etc.

2. Limit Exposure to Stressors

When possible, limit your exposure to stressful situations or triggers that exacerbate your OCD symptoms. (Remember, do NOT avoid them altogether.) For example, say you have contamination OCD, and your closest co-worker is a part-time gardener, so he almost always has dirty fingernails. This can activate your OCD, so ask your boss to move you to a different seat or room.

3. Develop Flexibility

You cannot control everything in life. Stress will always be there, not everything will always go according to plan, OCD boundaries will be crossed, etc. So, instead of being rigid about life, develop flexibility instead. Flexibility allows you to adjust your approach and cope effectively with new challenges. Yes, when life gives you lemons, make lemonade!

4. **Practice Mindfulness**
   Mindfulness helps you respond to stress and anxiety in a more balanced and controlled manner preventing a "bad day" from escalating into an OCD event. I want to stress that the goal is not just to incorporate mindfulness exercises. The goal is not to "do breathing exercises for 10 minutes every morning" but to become mindful 24/7.

5. **Practice Self-Care**
   Prioritize self-care activities that promote your well-being, such as regular exercise, sufficient sleep, healthy eating, and engaging in hobbies that bring you joy. (See also BPE and PLEASE, pages 56 and 62, respectively.)

   Take breaks from stressors and allow yourself time to recharge and rejuvenate. For example, if you're feeling overwhelmed, take a mental break, a digital break, or a whole day off.

6. **Establish a Support System**
   Reach out to friends, family, or support groups who understand your struggles with OCD. You can also join a group or community of people with OCD. Visit the International OCD Foundation, SupportGroups.com, or HealthUnlocked.com and see if these groups appeal to you. Having a reliable support system can provide encouragement and understanding during challenging times.

7. **Schedule Regular Check-Ins**
   Schedule periodic check-ins with yourself or a mental health professional to assess your progress, discuss challenges, etc.

   As part of my periodic check-ins with myself, I like to revisit my OCD triggers list, and I encourage you to do the same. This helps me become a bit more self-aware. However, don't dwell on the list. Go through it, and see if any trigger is presented during the day. If not, move on. If yes, then take out your "Coping Strategies Toolbox."

8. Develop a Coping Strategies Toolbox

Create a coping plan for whenever even the slightest OCD symptom rears its head. Of course, this is very personal, but I'm sharing my list below to give you an idea.

1. Practice Mindfulness (page 38). Square Breathing works best for me, but you can apply any mindfulness exercise. When I'm not in the mood for breathing exercises, I walk in nature for at least half an hour.
2. I do TIPP if I am still anxious (page 52), particularly intense exercising.
3. If my mind has entered the "obsessive" stage, i.e., when unwanted thoughts start to take hold, I do What to Do with THOUGHTS.

9. Create a Crisis Plan

Develop a plan for managing extreme moments of anxiety and distress. For example, create a list of emergency contacts, helplines, or crisis intervention services you can contact if needed.

10. Celebrate Progress!

Acknowledge and celebrate your progress in managing OCD and other life challenges. For example, if you're keeping a journal, write "YOU'RE AMAZING!" and record the progress that day. You can also give yourself meaningful rewards for reaching milestones or making progress in managing OCD. The rewards don't need to be extravagant; they can be as simple as treating yourself to a favorite meal, engaging in a hobby, or spending quality time with loved ones.

Conclusion: Living Life Beyond OCD

"You can thrive despite OCD.
It's about focusing on what you can control, finding joy in the present moment, and pursuing your passions."
— Chrissie Hodges

Living with OCD can be draining and difficult, but it doesn't mean it can't be meaningful and abundant as well. I've learned to reclaim my life and experience fulfillment during my healing journey. Of course, this transformation didn't happen overnight; it was a gradual process.

The best way I can explain it is that as I lifted each layer of OCD, I began to uncover deeper meaning and purpose in my life. The more I healed, the more I discovered "me," as I became more in tune with myself, I found a greater sense of purpose and clarity in my life.

Each step forward in healing brought me closer to the person I am. In turn, life seemed to unfold with new possibilities and opportunities. Embracing this process of self-discovery has made life more meaningful and rewarding than I ever thought possible. In short, I've switched from being OCD-focused to LIFE-focused. Here's how you can do the same:

Explore Interests and Passions

Before, my life revolved around obsessions and compulsions. It was like suffering from OCD tunnel vision. The first time I did the worksheet Build Positive Experiences (page 56), I couldn't even finish the list. That stumped me. Surely, I can list at least 10 things that make me happy! So I spent more time on it and remembered many activities and interests that brought me joy. One of them was old-school reading (paper, not digital). So, I bought books from my favorite authors, and I would spend hours reading. This "happy activity" was the one that made me begin to explore the possibility of writing on my own.

Identify Your Core Values

Reflect on the values that are most important to you. These could include compassion, creativity, connection, growth, or contributing to the well-being of others. Clarifying your values will guide your decisions and actions. As I learned more about myself, I realized I'm not just an "OCD person." I'm someone so much more than that. I can positively impact this world IF I want to and act on it.

Build Positive Relationships

OCD was one of the reasons I self-isolated for a while. Of course, the more I isolated, the more I felt lonely and cut off from the world, which exacerbated my OCD symptoms. As I engaged in CBT treatment and improved, I applied DBT's Interpersonal Effectiveness skills (page 69). I used them to find and cultivate meaningful connections with supportive and understanding people.

Set Goals and Aspirations, Dream, and Be "More"

I used to think that OCD defined who I was and thus limited what I could do in life. I no longer think that way at all! Yes, OCD can be an obstacle. But how big or trivial that obstacle depends on ME, so I don't let it limit me. So my final advice to you is to be limitless. Dream big, set achievable goals, and take action with the belief that you CAN overcome any obstacles that come your way.

Finding meaning and purpose is a personal and evolving process. Be patient with yourself and allow room for exploration and self-discovery. Beyond OCD, there is a vast world of opportunities and experiences waiting for you to explore, so embrace the journey with curiosity and openness, and gradually, you will discover new ways to experience a fulfilling and meaningful life.

Appendices

OCD Symptoms Checklist

The following checklist includes a range of common symptoms associated with OCD. Read each statement carefully and indicate the level of frequency or severity that best reflects your experiences. Remember, this checklist is not a diagnostic tool, but it can help you identify potential OCD symptoms and serve as a starting point for discussions with a mental health professional.

Instructions:

Choose the response that best depicts your experience during the last few weeks for each statement.

- **0** = Not at all
- **1** = Mildly
- **2** = Moderately
- **3** = Severely

OCD Symptom	Your Score
Experiencing persistent, intrusive thoughts or mental images that cause distress.	
Feeling compelled to engage in repetitive behaviors to reduce anxiety or prevent harm.	
Spending excessive time on rituals, such as washing, checking, or arranging things.	
Having a strong need for symmetry, order, or exactness.	
Being preoccupied with cleanliness, hygiene, or fear of contamination.	
Experiencing intrusive thoughts of harm or violence toward oneself or others.	
Constantly doubting or questioning actions, decisions, or thoughts.	
Engaging in mental rituals, such as counting, repeating words, or praying.	
Feeling a sense of incompleteness or discomfort when things are not just right.	
Avoiding specific situations, objects, or people due to obsessive fears.	
Experiencing distress when thoughts do not follow a specific pattern or sequence.	
Feeling a strong need for reassurance or seeking excessive reassurance from others.	
Having persistent doubts about one's memory or ability to remember things accurately.	
Engaging in mental checking or reviewing to alleviate uncertainty.	
Hoarding or being unable to discard items due to perceived value or fear of needing them later.	

OCD Symptom	Your Score
Experiencing intense fear of losing control or acting on unwanted thoughts.	
Feeling compelled to confess or confessing excessively to relieve guilt or anxiety.	
Engaging in superstitious or ritualistic behaviors to prevent harm or bad luck.	
Experiencing distressing or intrusive thoughts related to religious or moral concerns.	
Feeling a need to repeat specific actions until they are done "just right."	

Scoring:

- Add up your scores for each item to obtain a total score out of 60.
- The higher the score, the more likely it is that you may be experiencing symptoms associated with OCD.

Disclaimer: This checklist is only meant to help you determine if your feelings, thoughts, or actions are signs of OCD. It is NOT meant to be a diagnosis or a replacement for a review by a professional. Mental health problems can only be diagnosed by medical professionals who have been taught and are licensed to do so. Please talk to your doctor or a mental health worker about the results of this survey.

Also, if you scored "low" on this checklist but still think you might have OCD, please speak with a doctor or mental health professional for a proper diagnosis and advice.

OCD Self-Assessment Quiz

This self-assessment quiz is designed to help you evaluate the presence and severity of OCD symptoms you may be experiencing. Please read each statement carefully and select the response that best reflects your experiences over the past few weeks.

Quiz Questions:

1.) How often do you experience intrusive, unwanted thoughts, images, or impulses that cause distress or anxiety?

a.) Not at all

b.) Occasionally

c.) Several times a week

d.) Daily

2.) How much time do you spend engaging in repetitive behaviors or mental acts to alleviate distress or prevent harm?

a) None

b) Less than an hour per day

c) 1-3 hours per day

d) More than 3 hours per day

3.) Do you find it difficult to control or dismiss your obsessive thoughts?

a) Not at all

b) Sometimes

c) Often

d) Always

4.) How much do your obsessive thoughts and compulsive behaviors interfere with your daily functioning and activities?

a) Not at all
b) Mildly
c) Moderately
d) Significantly

5.) Are you frequently preoccupied with thoughts of contamination, germs, or cleanliness?

a) Not at all
b) Occasionally
c) Frequently
d) Constantly

6.) How often do you experience doubts and a strong need for reassurance or certainty?

a) Rarely
b) Sometimes
c) Often
d) Constantly

7.) Do you engage in repetitive checking behaviors (e.g., checking locks, appliances) to prevent harm or accidents?

a) Never
b) Rarely
c) Frequently
d) Compulsively

8.) How much distress do you experience when unable to perform a compulsive behavior or complete a ritual?

a) None
b) Mild distress
c) Moderate distress
d) Severe distress

9.) Are you bothered by intrusive thoughts of harming yourself or others, even though you have no intention of acting on them?

a) Not at all
b) Occasionally
c) Often
d) Constantly

10.) Have your symptoms been present for more than an hour a day and persisted for at least a few weeks?

a) No
b) Possibly
c) Yes, intermittently
d) Yes, consistently

Scoring: Please assign the following scores to your answers:

A answers: 0

B answers: 1

C answers: 2

D answers: 3

Scoring and Interpretation:

- Add up your scores for each question to obtain a total score out of 30.
- The higher the score, the more likely it is that you may be experiencing OCD symptoms.
- This quiz is not a diagnostic tool but can be a starting point for discussions with a mental health professional. If you have concerns about OCD, it is recommended to seek a formal evaluation.

Disclaimer: Please keep in mind that the only purpose of this quiz is to help you figure out if your emotions, thoughts, and/or behavior are signs of OCD. It is NOT meant to be a diagnosis or a substitute for a professional evaluation. Mental health problems can only be diagnosed by trained and licensed medical professionals. After you fill out this survey and figure out how to score it, please talk to your doctor or a mental health worker about the results.

Also, even if you scored "low" on the quiz but feel that you are suffering from OCD, please do not hesitate to consult with a healthcare provider or mental health specialist for an accurate assessment and guidance.

Know Your OCD Triggers

This exercise aims to help you identify your specific triggers—situations, thoughts, or emotions—that often lead to the onset of your OCD. Doing so promotes self-awareness and helps you anticipate and prepare for situations that might lead to your OCD symptoms.

Instructions:

1. **Create a Trigger Log.**
    a. Start by creating a trigger log. Divide a piece of paper or create a digital document with three columns: **Trigger**, **Obsessive Thought**, and **Compulsive Behavior**.
2. **Identify Triggers.**
    a. Reflect on your experiences and identify situations or circumstances that trigger your OCD symptoms. Triggers can be external (e.g., seeing dirt or encountering specific objects) or internal (e.g., experiencing anxiety or having specific thoughts).
    b. Write down each trigger in the "Trigger" column of the log. Be specific and detailed.
3. **Recognize Obsessive Thoughts.**
    a. For each trigger identified, note the specific obsessive thoughts that commonly arise concerning that trigger. Examples could include fears of contamination, doubts about safety, concerns about making mistakes, or intrusive thoughts about harm or violence.
    b. Write down the corresponding obsessive thoughts in the "Obsessive Thought" column of the log.
4. **Identify Compulsive Behaviors.**
    a. Next, identify the compulsive behaviors or rituals you typically engage in as a response to each obsessive thought or trigger. Compulsive behaviors can be overt actions (e.g., excessive handwashing, checking, arranging

items) or mental rituals (e.g., repeating phrases, counting in a specific pattern).

b. Write down the compulsive behaviors in the "Compulsive Behavior" column of the log.

5. **Review and Reflect.**

a. Take a step back and review the completed trigger log. Pay attention to patterns and commonalities across different triggers and related thoughts and behaviors.

b. Reflect on how these triggers and associated OCD symptoms impact your daily life, relationships, and overall well-being. Consider the distress and interference they cause.

My Trigger Log		
Trigger	**Obsessive Thought**	**Compulsive Behavior**
Example: Mom and Dad fighting, constantly screaming at each other	*Example: Something terrible will happen; maybe to them or maybe to me. I won't know when, but it WILL happen.* *If something bad happens to them, how will I survive?* *Who will care for me if something bad happens to me if they don't get along?*	*Example: Touching my parent's wedding picture repeatedly. No specific number of times, I just go on until I feel the world is "right" and "safe" again.*
Example: Co-workers having a heated argument	*Example: Something bad will happen at work, and I will be blamed for it. I will lose my job. What am I going to do then?*	*Example: I review my emails repeatedly to ensure I don't miss anything.* *I check and recheck completed tasks. And then check and recheck again.*

My Trigger Log		
Trigger	Obsessive Thought	Compulsive Behavior

A few notes:

- If you're working with a therapist, share your trigger log with them. If not, and you must share your trigger findings, discuss your log with someone you respect and trust.
- OCD triggers can change, so it may be helpful to revisit and update your trigger log over time as you gain more insight about yourself and your OCD.

Disclaimer: This exercise is intended only as a self-help tool. It isn't meant to substitute professional therapy. For a comprehensive treatment of OCD, please seek guidance from a mental health professional specializing in OCD treatment.

Exposure and Response Journal

This Exposure and Response Journal is to help you keep track of your thoughts, feelings, and anxiety levels while carrying out exposure strategies and keeping track of your progress.

Exposure and Response Journal	
Date: [Insert Date]	*Example: February 1*
Date:	
Trigger: [Describe the triggering situation, thought, or sensation that led to anxiety or distress.]	*Example: Approaching a door or entrance*
Trigger:	
Obsession: [Identify the specific obsessive thought that arose from the trigger.]	*Example: I fear something terrible will happen if I don't walk in a straight line to reach the door.*
Obsession:	
Compulsion: [Describe your compulsive behavior or response to reduce anxiety or distress.]	*Example: Walking in a straight line, ensuring my feet align with specific points on the floor until I reach the door.*
Compulsion:	

Exposure and Response Journal	
Anxiety Level (1-10): [Rate your anxiety level on a scale from 1 to 10, with 1 being minimal anxiety and 10 being extreme distress.]	*Example: 8/10*
Anxiety Level (1-10):	
Exposure Exercise: [Outline the steps you took to expose yourself to the trigger or anxiety-provoking situation intentionally. Describe how long you remained in the situation and what you did to resist the compulsion.]	*Example:* *Description: I walked towards the door without following my straight-line compulsion. I tried to walk freely and naturally, avoiding looking down.* *Thoughts: During the exercise, I consciously remind myself that nothing bad will happen if I don't walk in a straight line. I told myself there was no reasonable, logical link between "walking in a straight line" and something bad happening. I also tried to embrace the discomfort as part of the exposure process.*
Exposure Exercise:	
Anxiety Level During Exposure (1-10): [Rate your anxiety level on a scale from 1 to 10 during the exposure exercise.]	*Example: 8/10*
Anxiety Level During Exposure (1-10):	

Exposure and Response Journal	
Response Prevention: [Detail how you resisted the urge to engage in the compulsive behavior. Describe any strategies you used to prevent the compulsion.]	*Example:* *Whenever I felt the urge to look down or walk in a straight line, I counted my steps and focused on my breathing to distract myself. Breathe-step-breathe-step-breathe-step. I reminded myself that resisting the compulsion is part of the process.*
Response Prevention:	
Anxiety Level After Response Prevention (1-10): [Rate your anxiety level after resisting the compulsion on a scale from 1 to 10.]	*Example: 6/10*
Anxiety Level After Response Prevention (1-10):	
Reflections:	
Thoughts and Emotions: [Record any thoughts or emotions that arose during the exposure and response prevention process.]	*Example: During the exposure exercise, I felt very anxious and worried that something terrible would happen if I didn't walk in a straight line. The fear sometimes felt overwhelming, but I also noticed moments of curiosity and a desire to challenge the compulsion.*
Thoughts and Emotions:	

Exposure and Response Journal	
Physical Sensations: [Note any physical sensations you experienced during the exposure and response prevention, such as increased heart rate or tension.]	*Example: My heart was racing, and I felt tension in my shoulders and jaw. Resisting the urge to align my steps was challenging, but the tension gradually decreased as I continued.*
Physical Sensations:	
Challenges: [Identify any challenges you encountered during the exercise and how you worked through them.]	*Example: The most significant challenge was the fear that something bad would happen later if I didn't walk in a straight line. My mind kept coming up with worst-case scenarios. Still, I repeatedly reminded myself this was part of OCD and not based on reality.*
Challenges:	
Successes: [Highlight any successes or positive moments during the exposure and response prevention.]	*Example: I was surprised to have successfully walked halfway toward the door before succumbing to my straight-line compulsion. Even though I didn't make it all the way to the door, this was a significant accomplishment, considering how strong the urge to perform the compulsion was.*
Successes:	

Exposure and Response Journal	
Self-Encouragement: [Write words of self-encouragement and compassion for facing the trigger and resisting the compulsion.]	*Example: I'm proud of myself for facing this fear and stepping towards breaking free from OCD's grip. I realized I was stronger than I thought I was.*
Self-Encouragement:	
Plan for Future Exposures: [Consider what you can do differently or build upon for future exposure exercises.]	*Example: Next time, I'll try to increase the duration of the exposure exercise and continue resisting the compulsion. I won't stop until I reach that door!*
Plan for Future Exposures:	
Overall Experience: [Summarize your overall experience with the exposure and response prevention exercise, including any insights or learnings you gained.]	*Example: Challenging the need to walk in a straight line to reach the door was very difficult, but I am encouraged by my progress. It's empowering to confront my OCD and not let it control my actions. I look forward to more exposure exercises and using ERP to regain control over my life.*
Overall Experience:	

This journal is to help you track your progress in ERP and reinforce your commitment to facing OCD-related fears. Use it regularly to document your exposure exercises and response prevention efforts. Remember to celebrate your achievements, no matter how small, as each step brings you closer to gaining control over OCD and improving your quality of life.

Informing Others About Your OCD

This chapter addresses the important and often sensitive topic of informing others about your OCD. I guess the first question is, "Must you tell others?" No. You're not obligated in any way to inform others about your OCD. However, sharing this information with friends, family, or colleagues can be a significant step in seeking support and understanding for your condition.

Note that no one should force you to disclose your OCD. This is a personal decision; if and when you want to inform others, you must do so on your terms and in your time.

The following are some steps to consider when sharing information about your OCD. (**Tip**: Remember your Interpersonal Effectiveness training, page 69.)

1. **Choosing with whom to share.** Reflect on the right people to share your OCD journey with. Consider who you trust, who can offer understanding and empathy, who is willing to provide help and support, etc.

2. **Prepare for the conversation.**
    - Educate yourself about OCD. Help the person understand that OCD is a medical condition you cannot control or "snap out of."
    - Understand OCD symptoms, triggers, and treatment options to explain them accurately to others. Anticipate any questions or concerns the other person may have as well. For example, they might ask you what caused your OCD, how mild or severe your symptoms are, or what you're doing to treat it.
    - Create a list of common OCD myths and misconceptions and be prepared to talk about them. By informing the other person of what OCD is NOT, you create a more accurate and informed understanding of the condition.

3. **Choose the right time and place.** Find a calm and private setting to have an uninterrupted conversation with the person you want to inform about your OCD. Consider the other person's circumstances too. For example, don't try to have this conversation when they just got back from work, when they're dealing with something stressful, or when they are busy with other responsibilities.

4. **Communicate, not dictate.** Disclosing doesn't mean dominating the conversation. Remember to validate the other person by actively listening to their questions, paying attention to them when they're speaking, etc. (See also GIVE, page 78.)

5. **Prepare positive and negative reactions and responses.** Radically accept now that you'll receive positive *and* challenging reactions to your OCD disclosure. Prepare yourself for various reactions, including positive support, curiosity, lack of understanding, or even insensitivity.

   What do with negative responses?
   Try to **practice empathy**. Remember that this may be new or alien to others, so it's difficult for them to grasp what you're saying, let alone what you're going through. **Be patient** and consider that just because they don't understand now doesn't mean they won't understand and be supportive later.

   However, **prioritize yourself**. If the negative reaction proves to be too overwhelming for you, take a step back from the conversation. Think to yourself, "Okay, not today with this person," and say, "I feel that you're a bit taken aback and not ready to discuss my OCD right now, and that's perfectly fine. This is my journey. I will step away now and give us space to process this."

Negative reactions to your OCD disclosure are unpleasant, but I'm sure not everyone will react that way. So, instead of feeling bad about these responses, **focus on the positive and supportive responses you receive**. Embrace the understanding and empathy of those who show genuine care and concern.

6. **Express the OCD support you need.** Communicate how you want to be supported in your journey. Here are a few examples:
    - **Please listen.** You might want to ask others not to dismiss you or be nonchalant when experiencing symptoms.
    - **Please refrain from belittling or oversimplifying my condition.** You might want to ask others not to simplify or generalize your condition in their heads. (No, it's not *just* OCD.)
    - **Please be there when I need you.** You might want to ask others to be more accommodating when you send a message or call when experiencing symptoms.
    - **Please distract me.** You might want to ask certain people to be your fitness buddy, foodie friend, movie partner, etc., because these activities can be distracting and enjoyable, helping you reduce anxiety and provide a positive focus.

Disclosing Your OCD at Work: Should You or Shouldn't You?

Informing friends and family members about your OCD is one thing. Letting people know about your condition at work is another. Here are some things to think about:

1. **Work Culture.** What's the culture at your workplace? Is it a helpful, understanding, and nurturing one when it comes to mental health problems? Do you feel that it's a place that prioritizes the mental health of its employees?

2. **Work Impact.** Is OCD making it difficult for you to perform your job? If your symptoms make it hard for you to do your work duties, then it might be better to disclose your OCD to your boss or Human Resources so that something can be done to help you. Otherwise, your boss might see an employee who's not performing well.

3. **Trust and Support Levels at Work.** Reflect on how you get along with your coworkers and bosses. Do you trust at least some of them? Do you feel comfortable telling them about your OCD? Do you think they would be patient and helpful about your condition?

4. **Privacy Impact.** Think about how the change could affect your privacy. Once you tell people about your OCD, they will know about it and may have questions, concerns, or even misconceptions about it.

5. **Personal Impact.** Think about your personality or character. Are you someone who will feel relieved having disclosed your OCD at work, or someone who will constantly worry about how others perceive you? In short, will YOU feel better sharing your condition at work, or worse?

6. **Informing Means Adjusting.** If you decide to disclose your OCD at work, be ready to make adjustments from your side too. This could mean changing how you work at the office, being open to receiving help, willingness to seek professional help if your boss or the company requires it, etc.

7. **Legal protections.** Know the laws and rules that apply to mental health at your workplace. In many countries, it is against the law for a company to treat employees differently because of their mental health.

8. **Express the Support You Need.** Disclosing your condition at work is not just for "sharing purposes." The goal should be to get support so that you, in turn, can perform your work duties well. So, discuss the support you need and any other ways your boss or the company may help you. You can talk about moving to a quieter workspace to reduce triggers, flexible work hours, the possibility of working from home, requesting a meeting with co-workers to discuss things important to you and your OCD management, etc.

Remember that you don't have to tell anyone about your OCD if you feel uncomfortable or unsafe. If you're struggling about whether to disclose or not, seek advice from a mental health professional, support group, or someone you respect and trust to help you figure out what to do and how to deal with disclosing your OCD.

Bonus: Supporting Someone with OCD

Do you know someone with OCD? Please know that your support is an important factor in their journey. Here are some meaningful ways you can be there for them:

1. **Educate yourself about OCD.** You don't need to know everything, but it would help if you at least took the time to learn about the basics of OCD. Knowing more about this disorder will enable you to understand your loved one's experiences better.

2. **Be patient and non-judgmental.** OCD is a highly challenging condition. From the outside, OCD sufferers may look "quirky" at best, but inside, they are STRUGGLING, battling their own distressing thoughts and compulsive behaviors. So, please be patient and avoid passing judgment on their struggles. Show empathy and offer your support without criticism or impatience.

3. **Validate their feelings.** Validate the emotions your loved one experiences, even if you may not fully understand their thoughts and anxieties. Let them know that their feelings are valid and that you are there to support them throughout their journey.

4. **Actively listen to their journey.** Be an attentive, empathic, and non-judgmental listener. Let your loved one talk about their worries and feelings without stopping them. Don't minimize their experiences or give them quick fixes. Instead, give them a safe place to talk about how they feel.

5. **Be mindful of your words.** Please avoid making jokes about your loved one's struggles. Also, be mindful of the language you use when discussing OCD. Avoid stigmatizing or trivializing language and focus on creating a

compassionate and understanding atmosphere. Here are some phrases that people with OCD do NOT appreciate hearing.

"Why don't you just stop doing those rituals of yours?"
"It's all in your head!"
"Everyone's got a little bit of OCD."
"Can't you just chill out and stop worrying?"
"You think about things too much. Just let it go."
"Why don't you just try not to think about it?"
"Are you even trying NOT to think about it?"
"Toughen up; it's your mind. Control it."
"Just get over it."
"Just face your fears."
"Is this triggering you?"

6. **Normalize seeking treatment.** Many people with OCD find it difficult to talk about their conditions, let alone seek treatment. One way to help is to encourage your loved one to seek professional help and treatment for their OCD. Offer to go with them to therapy sessions or support groups if they feel comfortable. Assure them that seeking help is a sign of strength and that treatment can significantly improve their well-being.

7. **Help create a supportive environment.** Ensure your loved one is in a safe place where they feel understood and accepted when with you. Give practical help when needed, like helping with errands, words of encouragement when things are hard, etc.

8. **Respect their boundaries.** Respect the limits of your friend or family member, and don't force them to talk about their OCD if they aren't ready. Wait for them and let them speak at their own speed.

9. **Remember that support doesn't mean taking over.** Support does not imply authority. When you support someone, you offer advice, encouragement, and help. It's critical to empower your loved one to make their own decisions and take control of their OCD journey. Taking control may unintentionally harm their sense of autonomy, self-efficacy, and personal progress.

10. **Take care of yourself too!** Supporting someone with OCD can be emotionally demanding. Make sure you also take care of yourself by talking to your support system and learning how to deal with the difficulties of being a supportive colleague, friend, or family member.

The above-mentioned supportive strategies can make a positive difference in your loved one's life and contribute to their well-being as they navigate the complexities of living with OCD. Remember that your caring presence and understanding can be instrumental in their journey toward healing and recovery.

Additional Resources:

- Brain Lock, Twentieth Anniversary Edition: Free Yourself from Obsessive-Compulsive Behavior
- When a Family Member Has OCD: Mindfulness and Cognitive Behavioral Skills to Help Families Affected by Obsessive-Compulsive Disorder
- Overcoming Unwanted Intrusive Thoughts: A CBT-Based Guide to Getting Over Frightening, Obsessive, or Disturbing Thoughts
- Freedom from Obsessive Compulsive Disorder: A Personalized Recovery Program for Living with Uncertainty
- The Mindfulness Workbook for Ocd: A Guide to Overcoming Obsessions and Compulsions Using Mindfulness and Cognitive Behavioral Therapy

Review Request

If you enjoyed this book or found it useful...

I'd like to ask you for a quick favor:

Please share your thoughts and leave a quick REVIEW. Your feedback matters and helps me make improvements to provide the best books possible.

Reviews are so helpful to both readers and authors, so any help would be greatly appreciated! You can leave a review here:

https://tinyurl.com/ocd-workbook-review

Or by scanning the QR code below:

SCAN ME

Also, please join my ARC team to get early access to my releases.

https://barretthuang.com/arc-team/

THANK YOU!

Further Reading

Be sure to check out my other bestselling DBT books in the Mental Health Therapy series. Here are some of the titles you can find:

- DBT Workbook for Adults
- DBT Workbook for Kids
- DBT Workbook for Teens
- The DBT Anger Management Workbook
- DBT Workbook for PTSD
- DBT Workbook for BPD
- DBT Workbook for Depression
- DBT Workbook for Emotional Eating

You can get them here:

https://tinyurl.com/mental-health-therapy

SCAN ME

About the Author

Barrett Huang is an author and businessman. Barrett spent years discovering the best ways to manage his OCD, overcoming his anxiety, and learning to embrace life. Through his writing, he hopes to share his knowledge with readers, empowering people of all backgrounds with the tools and strategies they need to improve their mental wellbeing and be happy and healthy.

When not writing or running his business, Barrett loves to spend his time studying. He has majored in Psychology and completed the DBT skills certificate course by Dr. Marsha Linehan. Barrett's idol is Bruce Lee, who said, "The key to immortality is first living a life worth remembering."

Learn more about Barrett's books here:
https://barretthuang.com/

Index

References

1 Neustadt, G., Grados, M., & Samuels, J. F. (2010). Genetics of obsessive-compulsive disorder. *Psychiatric Clinics of North America, 33*(1), 141–158. https://doi.org/10.1016/j.psc.2009.11.001

2 Browne, H. A., Gair, S. L., Scharf, J. M., & Grice, D. E. (2014). Genetics of obsessive-compulsive disorder and related disorders. *Psychiatric Clinics of North America, 37*(3), 319–335. https://doi.org/10.1016/j.psc.2014.06.002

3 Krebs, G. C., Hannigan, L. J., Gregory, A. M., Rijsdijk, F. V., Maughan, B., & Eley, T. C. (2018). Are punitive parenting and stressful life events environmental risk factors for obsessive-compulsive symptoms in youth? A longitudinal twin study. *European Psychiatry, 56*(1), 35–42. https://doi.org/10.1016/j.eurpsy.2018.11.004

4 Carpenter, L., & Chung, M. C. (2011). Childhood trauma in obsessive compulsive disorder: The roles of alexithymia and attachment. *Psychology and Psychotherapy: Theory, Research and Practice, 84*(4), 367–388. https://doi.org/10.1111/j.2044-8341.2010.02003.x

5 Lissemore, J. I., Sookman, D., Gravel, P., Berney, A., Barsoum, A., Diksic, M., Nordahl, T. E., Pinard, G., Sibon, I., Cottraux, J., Leyton, M., & Benkelfat, C. (2018). Brain serotonin synthesis capacity in obsessive-compulsive disorder: Effects of cognitive behavioral therapy and sertraline. *Translational Psychiatry, 8*(1). https://doi.org/10.1038/s41398-018-0128-4

6 Biria, M., Banca, P., Healy, M. P., Keser, E., Sawiak, S. J., Rodgers, C. T., Rua, C., de Souza, A. M., Marzuki, A. A., Sule, A., Ersche, K. D., & Robbins, T. W. (2023). Cortical glutamate and GABA are related to compulsive behaviour in individuals with obsessive compulsive disorder and healthy controls. *Nature Communications, 14*(1). https://doi.org/10.1038/s41467-023-38695-z

7 Abramowitz, J. S., Khandker, M., Nelson, C. A., Deacon, B. J., & Rygwall, R. (2006). The role of cognitive factors in the pathogenesis of obsessive–compulsive symptoms: A prospective study. *Behaviour Research and Therapy, 44*(9), 1361–1374. https://doi.org/10.1016/j.brat.2005.09.011

8 Ramezani, Z., Rahimi, C., & Mohammadi, N. (2016). Predicting Obsessive Compulsive Disorder Subtypes Using Cognitive Factors. *Iranian journal of psychiatry, 11*(2), 75–81.

9 Team, S. (2023, January 24). *OCD Statistics 2020: Facts about obsessive-compulsive disorder*. The Checkup. https://www.singlecare.com/blog/news/ocd-statistics/#ocd-prevalence

10 Zauderer, S. (2023, January 11). *57+ OCD statistics: How many people have OCD?*. Life-Changing ABA Therapy - Cross River Therapy. https://www.crossrivertherapy.com/ocd-statistics

11 Brock, H., Hany, M. Obsessive-Compulsive Disorder. [Updated 2023 May 29]. In: StatPearls [Internet]. Treasure Island (FL): StatPearls Publishing; 2023 Jan-. Available from: https://www.ncbi.nlm.nih.gov/books/NBK553162/

12 Zauderer, S. (2023, January 11). *57+ OCD statistics: How many people have OCD?*. Life-Changing ABA Therapy - Cross River Therapy. https://www.crossrivertherapy.com/ocd-statistics

13 Linehan, M. (2021). *Building a Life Worth Living: A Memoir*. Random House.

14 Carey, B. (2011, June 23). *Expert on mental illness reveals her own fight*. The New York Times. https://www.nytimes.com/2011/06/23/health/23lives.html

15 Abramowitz, J. S. (2006). The psychological treatment of obsessive—compulsive disorder. *The Canadian Journal of Psychiatry*, *51*(7), 407–416. https://doi.org/10.1177/070674370605100702

16 O'Neill, J., & Feusner, J. (2015). Cognitive-behavioral therapy for obsessive-compulsive disorder: Access to treatment, prediction of long-term outcome with neuroimaging. *Psychology Research and Behavior Management*, 211. https://doi.org/10.2147/prbm.s75106

17 Ahovan, M., Balali, S., Abedi Shargh, N., & Doostian, Y. (2016). Efficacy of dialectical behavior therapy on clinical signs and emotion regulation in patients with obsessive-compulsive disorder. *Mediterranean Journal of Social Sciences*. https://doi.org/10.5901/mjss.2016.v7n4p412

18 Twohig, M. P., & Smith, B. M. (2015). Targeting the function of inner experiences in obsessive compulsive and related disorders. *Current Opinion in Psychology*, *2*, 32–37. https://doi.org/10.1016/j.copsyc.2014.12.033

19 Hayes, S. C., & Hofmann, S. G. (2017). The third wave of cognitive behavioral therapy and the rise of process-based care. *World Psychiatry*, *16*(3), 245–246. https://doi.org/10.1002/wps.20442

20 Ito, E., Shima, R., & Yoshioka, T. (2019). A novel role of oxytocin: Oxytocin-induced well-being in humans. *Biophysics and Physicobiology, 16*, 132–139. https://doi.org/10.2142/biophysico.16.0_132

21 *Serotonin: What is it, Function & Levels*. Cleveland Clinic. (n.d.). Retrieved March 1, 2023, from https://my.clevelandclinic.org/health/articles/22572-serotonin

22 Zanon, C., Hutz, C. S., Reppold, C. T., & Zenger, M. (2016). Are happier people less vulnerable to rumination, anxiety, and post-traumatic stress? evidence from a large scale disaster. *Psicologia: Reflexão e Crítica, 29*(1). https://doi.org/10.1186/s41155-016-0038-4

23 Pally, R., & Olds, D. (2018). Emotional processing: The mind-body connection. *The Mind-Brain Relationship*, 73–104. https://doi.org/10.4324/9780429482465-4

24 Schuch, F. B., Vancampfort, D., Richards, J., Rosenbaum, S., Ward, P. B., & Stubbs, B. (2016). Exercise as a treatment for depression: A meta-analysis adjusting for publication bias. *Journal of Psychiatric Research, 77*, 42–51. https://doi.org/10.1016/j.jpsychires.2016.02.023

25 Watson, N. F., Badr, M. S., Belenky, G., Bliwise, D. L., Buxton, O. M., Buysse, D., Dinges, D. F., Gangwisch, J., Grandner, M. A., Kushida, C., Malhotra, R. K., Martin, J. L., Patel, S. R., Quan, S., & Tasali, E. (2015). Recommended amount of sleep for a healthy adult: A joint consensus statement of the American Academy of Sleep Medicine and Sleep Research Society. *SLEEP*. https://doi.org/10.5665/sleep.4716

26 Willner, P., & Goodey, R. (2006). Interaction of cognitive distortions and cognitive deficits in the formulation and treatment of obsessive-compulsive behaviours in a woman with an intellectual disability. *Journal of Applied Research in Intellectual Disabilities, 19*(1), 67–73. https://doi.org/10.1111/j.1468-3148.2005.00279.x

27 Jónsson, H., Hougaard, E., & Bennedsen, B. E. (2011). Dysfunctional beliefs in group and individual cognitive behavioral therapy for obsessive compulsive disorder. *Journal of Anxiety Disorders, 25*(4), 483–489. https://doi.org/10.1016/j.janxdis.2010.12.001

28 Owen Kelly, P. (2020, November 13). *Common Cognitive Distortions in OCD*. Verywell Mind. https://www.verywellmind.com/cognitive-distortions-and-ocd-2510477

29 Law, C., & Boisseau, C. L. (2019). Exposure and response prevention in the treatment of obsessive-compulsive disorder: Current perspectives. *Psychology Research and Behavior Management, Volume 12*, 1167–1174. https://doi.org/10.2147/prbm.s211117

30 Ferrando, C., & Selai, C. (2021). A systematic review and meta-analysis on the effectiveness of exposure and response prevention therapy in the treatment of obsessive-compulsive disorder. *Journal of Obsessive-Compulsive and Related Disorders, 31*, 100684. https://doi.org/10.1016/j.jocrd.2021.100684

31 Song, Y., Li, D., Zhang, S., Jin, Z., Zhen, Y., Su, Y., Zhang, M., Lu, L., Xue, X., Luo, J., Liang, M., & Li, X. (2022). The effect of exposure and response prevention therapy on obsessive-compulsive disorder: A systematic review and meta-analysis. *Psychiatry Research, 317*, 114861. https://doi.org/10.1016/j.psychres.2022.114861

32 Lambert, M. (2008, July 1). *APA releases guidelines on treating obsessive-compulsive disorder*. American Family Physician. https://www.aafp.org/pubs/afp/issues/2008/0701/p131.html

33 *How is OCD treated?*. International OCD Foundation. (n.d.). https://iocdf.org/about-ocd/ocd-treatment/

34 Starcevic, V., Berle, D., Brakoulias, V., Sammut, P., Moses, K., Milicevic, D., & Hannan, A. (2011). The nature and correlates of avoidance in obsessive–compulsive disorder. *Australian & New Zealand Journal of Psychiatry, 45*(10), 871–879. https://doi.org/10.3109/00048674.2011.607632

Made in the USA
Middletown, DE
29 October 2024

63507170R00108